Lernkrimi Englisch

Die Spur des Höllen- hundes

Story: Marc Hillefeld
Übersetzung: Emily A. Grosvenor

Compact Verlag

Bisher sind in dieser Reihe erschienen:
- Compact Lernkrimi Englisch Grammatik
- Compact Lernkrimi Englisch Konversation
- Compact Lernkrimi Englisch Grundwortschatz
- Compact Lernkrimi Englisch Aufbauwortschatz
- Compact Lernkrimi Französisch Grammatik
- Compact Lernkrimi Französisch Grundwortschatz
- Compact Lernkrimi Italienisch Grammatik
- Compact Lernkrimi Italienisch Grundwortschatz
- Compact Lernkrimi Spanisch Grammatik
- Compact Lernkrimi Spanisch Grundwortschatz

In der Reihe Lernthriller sind erschienen:
- Compact Lernthriller Englisch Grammatik
- Compact Lernthriller Englisch Konversation
- Compact Lernthriller Englisch Grundwortschatz
- Compact Lernthriller Englisch Aufbauwortschatz

Weitere Titel sind in Vorbereitung.

© 2004 Compact Verlag München
Alle Rechte vorbehalten. Nachdruck, auch auszugsweise,
nur mit ausdrücklicher Genehmigung des Verlages gestattet.
Chefredaktion: Evelyn Boos
Redaktion: Brigitte Stoffel
Fachredaktion: Autumn Pierce
Produktion: Wolfram Friedrich
Titelillustration: Karl Knospe
Typografischer Entwurf: Maria Seidel
Umschlaggestaltung: Carsten Abelbeck

ISBN: 3-8174-7307-9
7273075

Besuchen Sie uns im Internet: www.compactverlag.de

Vorwort

Mit dem neuen, spannenden Compact Lernkrimi können Sie Ihre Englischkenntnisse auf schnelle und einfache Weise vertiefen, auffrischen und überprüfen.

Inspector Hudson erleichtert das Sprachtraining mit Action und Humor. Er und seine mysteriösen Kriminalfälle stehen im Mittelpunkt einer zusammenhängenden Story.

Der Krimi wird auf jeder Seite durch abwechslungsreiche und kurzweilige Übungen ergänzt, die das Lernen unterhaltsam und spannend machen.

Prüfen Sie Ihr Englisch in Lückentexten, Zuordnungs- und Übersetzungsaufgaben, in Buchstabenspielen und Kreuzworträtseln!

Ob im Bus oder in der Bahn, im Wartezimmer, zu Hause oder in der Mittagspause – das Sprachtraining im handlichen Format bietet die ideale Trainingsmöglichkeit für zwischendurch.

Schreiben Sie die Lösungen einfach ins Buch!

Die richtigen Antworten sind in einem eigenen Lösungsteil zusammengefasst.

Und nun kann die Spannung beginnen …

Viel Spaß und Erfolg!

Inhalt

Story

James Hudson arbeitet als Inspector bei der legendären Polizeibehörde Scotland Yard. Er ist einer der fähigsten Männer und wird immer dann zu Rate gezogen, wenn seine Kollegen mal wieder vor einem Rätsel stehen. Seine resolute und krimibegeisterte Haushälterin Miss Paddington unterstützt ihn stets mit liebevoller Fürsorge. Und insgeheim verfolgt sie noch ein weiteres Ziel: ihn endlich mit der jungen, attraktiven Versicherungsagentin Elvira Elliot zu verkuppeln.

Hudson gewinnt ein Rätselwochenende auf dem sagenumwobenen Schloss Bludstone. In traumhafter Hotelatmosphäre soll für die geladenen Gäste ein Mord vorgetäuscht werden; doch es kommt anders. Was als Spaß gedacht war, wird bitterer Ernst …
Welches Geheimnis birgt das alte Schloss? Was steckt hinter der Legende des grausamen Höllenhundes? Wer trägt die Schuld an dem schrecklichen Verbrechen?
Nach und nach gelingt es Inspector Hudson, Licht in das Dunkel des Unerklärlichen zu bringen …

On the Trail of the Hound from Hell

The scream was bone-chilling and ripped Inspector James Hudson out of his deepest dreams. Only someone in fear of death would scream like that!

The inspector opened his eyes and oriented himself as quickly as possible. Although he had just been sleeping quite peacefully, his instincts were wide awake.

The scream was still resonating in the stairway as Hudson ran down the steps to the ground floor. The early light of morning was shining through the window as he grabbed an umbrella from the stand.

The scream came from the kitchen. Hudson knew that his housekeeper, Miss Paddington, was, as usual, preparing an elaborate breakfast at this early hour of the morning on Saturday. Had she been attacked by burglars?

Übung 1: Finden Sie die richtige Antwort!

1. What's your name?
   a) ☐ My name is James Hudson.
   b) ☐ You call me James Hudson.

2. How old are you?
   a) ☐ I have thirty-four.
   b) ☐ I am thirty-four.

3. What is your profession?
   a) ☐ I do the inspector for Scotland Yard.
   b) ☐ I am an inspector at Scotland Yard.

4. Do you speak English?
   a) ☐ Yes, I do.
   b) ☐ Yes, I am speaking English.

5. Where were you born?
   a) ☐ I am born of London.
   b) ☐ I was born in London.

6. Do you like your job?
   a) ☐ Yes, I like it very much.
   b) ☐ Yes, I am liking it very much.

Hudson feared the worst. For a moment, he cursed himself for leaving his weapon in a desk drawer at Scotland Yard, out of principle. He could really use it right now. Hudson held tightly to the umbrella, breathed deeply and stepped through the door to the kitchen. The door hit the sink with a loud bang.
Miss Paddington let out a sharp, shocked scream. A pot with porridge fell to the floor with a rattle.

Übung 2: Welches Wort ist das „schwarze Schaf"?

1. bang, rattle, resonate, curse, noise _____
2. elaborate, fancy, simple, intricate _____
3. umbrella, door, sink, grab _____
4. instinct, breathe, gasp, sigh _____
5. burglar, thief, criminal, housekeeper _____
6. shocked, peaceful, tranquill, quiet _____

Inspector Hudson looked around and saw no one, apart from Miss Paddington.

Next to the stove, the small kitchen radio was playing.

"James!" called Miss Paddington. "My God, did you frighten me! What has got into you?"

The inspector swallowed.

"And next Saturday – the amazing finale of 'Murder at Noon'. Be there!" demanded the voice from the radio.

"Miss Paddington," Hudson gasped, "I heard a scream and thought that something had happened to you."

The old lady shook her head disapprovingly. "James, you are just too nervous. You know that I always listen to my mystery programme on Saturday while I am preparing your breakfast."

Übung 3: Ergänzen Sie die passende Berufsbezeichnung!

1. He investigates crimes.

2. She cleans the house and prepares food.

3. He announces the songs on the radio.

4. She evaluates insurance claims.

5. He decides questions of law.

ÜBUNG 3

"Well okay," she admitted, shrugging her shoulders.

"Maybe I turned it up a little too loud during the fight-scene."

Hudson laid the umbrella down beside him and sunk into one of the kitchen chairs.

Übung 4: Welcher Satz enthält die richtige Zeitform?

1. Hudson las die Zeitung, während sie das Frühstück vorbereitete.
   a) ☐ Hudson reads the paper while she was preparing breakfast.
   b) ☐ Hudson had read the paper while she has prepared breakfast.
   c) ☐ Hudson read the paper while she was preparing breakfast.

2. Der Krach in der Küche hatte ihn aus seinem tiefen Schlaf gerissen.
   a) ☐ The noise in the kitchen woke him from his deep sleep.
   b) ☐ The noise in the kitchen wakes him from his deep sleep.
   c) ☐ The noise in the kitchen had woken him from his deep sleep.

Well, at least he was awake now. Miss Paddington's radio programmes were better than any alarm clock.

Übung 5: Unterstreichen Sie die Verben!

He wiped the sweat from his brow. Miss Paddington stepped towards him and held out a cup of tea, which the inspector thankfully accepted. The aromatic steam of his favourite Earl Grey calmed him at once.

"I don't understand," he said between each enjoyable sip, "how this nonsense can excite you, my dear."

"And I don't understand, James, how you foster such dislike to mysteries."

"It is quite simple, Miss Paddington," James answered. "Most murder mystery novels … or radio programmes … miss reality by a mile. True police work consists of the laborious and exact search for facts. If mystery novels were to show reality, they would have to be a thousand pages thick and so boring that no one would read them."

The inspector took another sip of tea and leaned back.

Übung 6: Wie lautet der Komparativ?

1. I am doing much _____ (good) at investigating.

2. She is _____ (smart) than all of her siblings.

3. Are you a _____ (quick) runner than he is?

4. He gets up _____ (early) on weekdays.

5. She lives _____ (far) away than it seemed.

6. He makes _____ (much) mistakes than he should.

"And besides which – an engineer doesn't read construction plans after work. Why should I worry myself any more about crimes in my free time – even if they are fiction? And –"

Miss Paddington tapped her finger on her lips.

"Psst, James, here comes the riddle. I'm not allowed to miss that."

"Riddle?" James questioned. „What in the world is that supposed to be?"

The radio answered the inspector's question.

"With today's question you can win another great prize. Today we are giving away an exciting mystery weekend for two at Castle

Bludstone. Please listen to the question and call us! Now … listen up!"

Hudson shook his head.

"A mystery weekend? What in the world is that? What could that be?"

Sometimes, the inspector was amazed at how fascinated mankind was with crime.

"Psst!" hissed Miss Paddington.

From the radio came a dramatic melody.

"What is the title of the Sherlock Holmes story in which he hunts down a four legged evil-doer through night and fog? If you know it, call us right now!"

Miss Paddington stood spellbound in front of the receiver and smacked her hand on her forehead.

ÜBUNG 7 !

Übung 7: Setzen Sie die Verben in die richtige Zeitform!

"Oh my God," she called out. "Sherlock Holmes? I am afraid that's a question I cannot answer."

Inspector Hudson couldn't (1. hold back) _____ a laugh.

"That is simple, my dear Miss Paddington," he said nasally. "Naturally, they (2. talk about) _____ Sir Arthur Conan Doyle's Hound of the Baskervilles, from 1901. Maybe you (3. shall) _____ have a look at the classics in your mystery library, Miss –"

But Miss Paddington (4. do) _____ not wait until the

inspector had finished the sentence. She (5. stumble) _____

_____ past the inspector into the hall.

Hudson (6. sigh) _____ and took another sip of tea. A few

seconds later, he heard Miss Paddington's voice on the radio.

"Hel-lo? Am I on the radio?" she asked excitedly.

"Yes, you (7. be) _____, my dear. Welcome to Mystery on

Saturday!" greeted the radio announcer.

"(8. to know) _____ the answer to our prize question?"

"Oh God oh God oh God!" puffed Miss Paddington. "I'm so excited!"
"Well?" asked the announcer.
"Uhhm ... Yes, surely. The story is called The Hound of Basketville,
oh no, of Baskervilles."
A noise sounded. The inspector laughed.
"Congratulations!" yelled the announcer. "The answer is right on
target! The mystery weekend belongs to you and a companion!"
"Yippee!" Miss Paddington shouted. "Thank you, James!" called
Miss Paddington through the radio.

Übung 8: Beantworten Sie die Fragen zum Text!

1. What doesn't the inspector like about mystery novels?

_____

2. Explain the noises that startled the inspector at the beginning.

_____

! ÜBUNG 8

3. What personal quality makes the inspector approach the kitchen so cautiously?

_____

4. What Arthur Conan Doyle novel does the inspector correctly name?

_____

5. Does Miss Paddington actually get the question right?

_____

The announcer asked Miss Paddington to stay on the line for a bit so that he could take down her personal ~~information~~. A couple of minutes later, the housekeeper walked into the kitchen, beaming with joy.

"Congratulations, Miss Paddington," laughed Hudson. "I think you got a direct hit there."

"Thanks for your help, James. But tell me, why are you so familiar with these old stories. I thought you hated mysteries?"

The inspector shrugged his shoulders.

"True, but the stories of Sir Arthur Conan Doyle really do belong to the classics. I gobbled them up as a child and always admired Sherlock Holmes's sharp thinking skills."

!

ÜBUNG 9

Übung 9: Formulieren Sie im Passiv!

1. The announcer took down her personal information.

_____

2. The inspector gobbled up mysteries as a child.

_____

3. The inspector supplied the answer to the riddle.

_____

4. The housekeeper cooked the breakfast.

_____

5. Miss Paddington answered the announcer's question.

_____

6. She picked up the receiver with anticipation.

_____

7. Hudson closed the door quietly.

_____

Übung 10: Welche Wörter gehören in die Lücken? **(commit, protection, apparently, stood, inattentive, grumbling, thereafter)**

ÜBUNG 10 !

Miss Paddington grinned.

"Well then, remind me to go by Mr Doyle's gravestone occasionally and lay down some flowers in thanks."

Suddenly, a low 1. _____ sounded from the kitchen.

"Oops, I'm afraid that was my stomach," said the inspector. "How would you like to take care of the living for now and put a few pieces of toast on my plate, my dear?"

"Surely, James, excuse me. How 2. _____ of me."

Miss Paddington returned to the preparation of the elaborate Saturday breakfast.

Shortly 3. _____ the scrambled eggs, bacon, ham, and bread began to pile up in front of the inspector.

"Tell me," asked the inspector while he enjoyed his breakfast, "with whom do you want to go to this mystery weekend? With a girlfriend?"

Luckily, the housekeeper 4. _____ at the stove at this moment, with her back to the inspector. Otherwise her impish smile wouldn't have got past him.

"Yes, that's it exactly," she said softly. "Girlfriend is exactly the right word …"

The next two weeks flew by for the inspector. The unusual crimes – Inspector Hudson's special area – seemed to pile up in the London autumn. 5. _____ the thick autumn fog called the crooks out of their houses, so that they could 6. _____ their crimes in the 7. _____ of the early dawn.

Inspector James Hudson solved the case of the living wax figures, delivered a trixter, who had tried to sell the crown jewels …
In short, just two normal weeks in the career of an inspector.
And so, James Hudson was amazed, when Miss Paddington one morning – it was Saturday again – walked into the kitchen with a big suitcase.
The inspector put down his teacup and sprang up to help the old lady with her baggage.

Übung 11: Setzen Sie die Verben in die Sätze ein!
(commenced, made, interrogated, searched, solved, cast, caused)

1. The inspector had _____ many cases.

2. Her testimony _____ doubt on her brother's statement.

3. The woman _____ the accusation earlier that day.

4. Hudson _____ the witnesses one by one.

5. Later that evening, he _____ for important clues.

6. The murder _____ great alarm in the neighbourhood.

7. Instead of following the normal routine, he _____ questioning right away.

"Miss Paddington, if you had said something, I would have carried the bag downstairs for you!"
Miss Paddington waved him away.
"It's fine, James, I've got it."
But the inspector would not let himself be misled and took the suitcase from the housekeeper.
"My Lord is that heavy," he gasped, laughingly. "Do you want to travel?"
Then suddenly, it struck him.
Of course, the 'Mystery Weekend' that his housekeeper had won two weeks before.
"That's true! You are leaving me today for the weekend. How could I forget?"
Miss Paddington looked bashfully at the floor.

Übung 12: Welche Gegenteile gehören zusammen? Setzen Sie die passenden Ziffern ein!

1. quiet
2. seldom
3. wrinkled
4. answer
5. noise
6. light
7. weekend

☐ smooth
☐ loud
☐ silence
☐ often
☐ question
☐ weekday
☐ dark

"No, James, that's not quite true. You know that it was a weekend for two, and then I thought … well, in this suitcase I have packed a few things for yourself …"

The inspector was silent.

"For me? Does that mean that you planned for me to be your companion?"

"Oh, please don't say no, James," begged Miss Paddington and glanced at the inspector.

James Hudson sighed. He had variety enough with his job. What he really needed was peace and tranquillity. But he couldn't deny Miss Paddington's pleading glance. "Well then, it may seem a little bit surprising but why not – I'm there!"

Miss Paddington cheered up.

"Great, James! It will definitely be a lot of fun!"

"Mmmh," mumbled the inspector, a bit sceptical, "but what exactly is this 'Mystery Weekend'?"

Miss Paddington sank wheezing into the chair and poured herself some tea.

"It's quite simple. A couple of paying guests enjoy a lovely but exciting weekend in the countryside in a fine and luxurious hotel …"

Übung 13: Übersetzen Sie die Sätze!

1. Miss Paddington gewann den Preis, indem sie die Frage richtig beantwortete.

   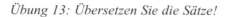

2. Hudson zieht es vor, seine Arbeit im Büro liegen zu lassen.

3. Miss Paddington hatte seinen Koffer schon gepackt.

4. Es wird bestimmt ganz lustig werden!

5. Er wollte den Koffer für sie tragen, aber sie hat es alleine geschafft.

"Up until now, it sounds quite good," Hudson smirked.

"Some of the employees are actors who enact a murder. The participants in the mystery then try to unmask the "murderer" through a search for clues and interrogation."

Hudson shook his head. Once again, this fascination with crime. But if Miss Paddington gets some kind of joy out of it … why not?

"Sounds … interesting," he said carefully.

"Exactly. And besides, whoever solves the murder mystery wins a special prize!"

"I understand," he nodded laughingly. "And you hope that I, as a professional agent, can hit the target, right?"

Miss Paddington shrugged her shoulders innocently.

"Oh, it has nothing to do with that. But if you should just by chance happen to discover who the murderer is ... just look at it as a challenge. In any case, you can measure your criminal understanding against that of a bunch of amateurs."

Hudson grinned and clapped his hands.

ÜBUNG 14

Übung 14: Schreiben Sie die Zahlen aus!

1. 14.53 Pounds _____

2. $236.78 _____

3. 9,412 _____

4. $4\frac{3}{4}$ _____

5. 16/11/2002 _____

"Wonderful!" he said. "When do we leave?"

Miss Paddington looked at the floor again.

"Oh, I think I have forgotten to tell you something, James ..."

"Really? What then?"

"Oh, I have so much housework to do and this damp fog isn't good for my old bones and so I thought ... maybe you should just go with ... well ..."

Hudson put down his teacup and looked at his embarrassed housekeeper sternly.

"Miss Paddington," he said, "what have you come up with this time? Who is to be my companion?"

"I ... well ... uhhm ..." she beat around the bush.

Suddenly, the doorbell rang.

Not just once, but several times, in the rhythm of a well-known children's song.

"Ah, that will be her!" called Miss Paddington, as she sprang up relieved and ran to the front door.

"Her?!" Hudson called after her. "Miss Paddington, who did you get me …"

"Hello James," a voice called to him. "What, you're not ready yet? Hurry up a bit, or else we will miss the murder!"

The inspector's jaw dropped.

Directly in front of him, grinning and wearing a fancy leather suit, stood Elvira Elliot.

Übung 15: Welche Antwort passt?

A m

1. Hi Elvira, how's it going?
    a) ☐ Great! Let's stop on our way there.
    b) ☐ Good, how are you?
    c) ☐ Fine, if you like.

2. Are you looking forward to the trip?
    a) ☐ Sure I am! I really need a vacation.
    b) ☐ I guess I'll see you there.
    c) ☐ Thanks, I got it from my parents.

3. How is the insurance business going?
    a) ☐ I am well, but a little tired.
    b) ☐ Very well, business is booming, but it can be stressful at times.
    c) ☐ Well enough. Last week we had our first club meeting.

4. Is that a new suit you are wearing?
   a) ☐ Yes, nice of you to notice!
   b) ☐ No, I can't be there.
   c) ☐ Yes, actually, it didn't fit that well at all.

"Have fun, James! And don't be mad, you'll surely have a great time!"
Miss Paddington stood in the doorway and waved at the inspector,
while Elvira drove her sports car out of the entrance.
"Don't be mad? What did your Miss Paddington mean by that,
James?" Elvira asked.
"My Miss Paddington neglected to tell me that she had intended
this Mystery Weekend for the two of us, Elvira."
Elvira laughed out loud.
"I get it. The lovely old lady is trying once again to bring us
together. How sweet of her!"

Übung 16: Wählen Sie die passende Aussage aus!

1. Miss Paddington won a mystery weekend at a castle.
   a) ☐ Congratulations!
   b) ☐ Happy Birthday!

2. Inspector Hudson solved a case.
   a) ☐ Good day!
   b) ☐ Good work!

3. Two of Hudson's friends are celebrating the day they got married.
   a) ☐ Happy anniversary!
   b) ☐ Happy wedding day!
   c) ☐ Congratulations on your wedding!

It was indeed not the first time that Miss Paddington had tried to do something of the kind. Of course, he liked Elvira quite a lot and her position as an insurance agent had allowed them to solve many cases together. But if he was seriously interested in Elvira, then he would have taken the first step himself. In the end, he was an adult man and had braved other dangers!

Elvira appeared to be reading his thoughts.

"No worrying, James. Just enjoy the weekend. I am sure that we will get along gloriously together. And Castle Bludstone is a first-class hotel, murder mystery or not. You will like it."

Übung 17: Setzen Sie die richtigen Pronomen in die Lücken ein!

"Let's hope so, by goodness!" replied the inspector, not quite convinced.

But when he was honest with 1._____, he found the idea of spending a peaceful weekend in the country with 2._____ not unpleasant at all.

The drive to the lonesome and idyllic castle was uneventful. Miss Paddington had packed 3._____ a big lunch basket and the lovely weather invited 4._____ to a picnic at the side of the road. The October sun was still shining around noon and Inspector Hudson felt more relaxed than 5._____ had felt for a long time. Maybe he had done 6._____ an injustice, and this short vacation was a wonderful idea.

It was afternoon before the dark clouds came into view. Every now and then 7. _____ passed a small town, but soon, the roads were completely free of people. A thick fog swept in and enshrouded the Northern English hills.

"What a pea-souper," cursed Elvira grudgingly and took 8. _____ _____ down a gear. "It looks like we have left the good weather behind us. How far is it from here, James?"

!
ÜBUNG 18

*Übung 18: Formulieren Sie die Sätze auf Englisch mit **let's (let us)**!*

1. Gehen wir ein bisschen weiter.

   _____

2. Machen wir ein Picknick!

   _____

3. Warten wir, bis das Wetter besser ist.

   _____

4. Fahren wir doch ein wenig langsamer, Elvira.

   _____

5. Schauen wir schnell auf die Landkarte, ob diese Straße stimmt.

   _____

"It can't be much farther than this. Next we will drive through a dangerous moor, right behind which we will find Castle Bludstone."

"Right behind sounds good," she complained and threw the map on the inspector's lap. "I haven't seen a human soul for hours. Are you sure that we haven't got lost, James?"

In front of them, in the thick fog, stood a surreal creature on the street. It waved at them.

"Elvira, watch out!" screamed the inspector.

A split second later, Elvira slammed on the brakes.

The car screeched to a stop.

"There you have your human soul," said the inspector, pointing to the figure, which stood just a metre from the hood. Despite Elvira's reckless braking, the figure had not moved an inch from where it stood.

"Man, are you crazy?" she yelled, still shaking. "I almost ran right over you!"

Übung 19: Schreiben Sie die Sätze in höflicher Form!

1. Elvira! Don't drive so recklessly!

2. Roll down the door windows and look at the guy.

3. Give me your baggage and coats.

4. Grab that bag of yours and throw it over to me.

5. Get over to the side of the road!

The inspector unbuckled himself and stepped *climbed* out of the passenger seat.

"Calm down, Elvira," the inspector said. "Perhaps the man needs help. Why else would he be standing on the road in the middle of the fog?"

The man was wearing a country tweed suit, with coarse plaid and a cap of the same pattern, under which red curls flowed out. The man's coarse face had reddened as well. Although he had just barely escaped being run over, he showed absolutely no emotion. He nodded to the inspector.

ÜBUNG 20 !

Übung 20: Um welches Kleidungsstück handelt es sich?

1. A one piece, elegant outfit for a woman.
2. The kind of fabric famous by the Scottish.
3. A wool blend often worn in Scotland.
4. Synonym for a coat.
5. Clothing material made from an animal's skin.
6. Piece of clothing worn around the neck.
7. Another word for a hat.
8. Short and long clothes for your legs.

"Thank you for stopping," was all that he said.

"Well sure, we hardly had any other choice, my dear fellow," Hudson said. "My name is James Hudson, by the way."

Hudson saw no occasion to mention his full title here in the outback. Anyway, he was on vacation. He held out his hand to the stranger, who ignored it completely, but nodded his head.

"Miles O'Malley."

Not an especially friendly greeting, thought the inspector.

Übung 21: Ordnen Sie den Fragen passende Antworten zu!

1. Are you ready?
2. How are you doing today?
3. Hello, it's so nice to see you.
4. How was your trip?
5. Tell me, did you find the house easily?
6. Do you remember me?

☐ Great! The weather was very good.
☐ Wonderful, thank you.
☐ Likewise. It's been so long!
☐ Yes. The directions were fine.
☐ No, wait just a second, please.
☐ Yes, sure, we met last summer.

O'Malley pointed back over his shoulder.

"My car gave out. The battery. This damn wet fog makes everything fall apart."

The inspector looked through the fog.

He could see the outlines of an old car on the side of the road, like a ghost.

"Elvira, do you have jumper cables in your boot?" he asked her, who had got out of the car.

The insurance agent stepped forward and went without saying hello. O'Malley seemed fine with that.

"Sure. I'll drive the car forward a bit, so that we can help start you up."

One minute later, Elvira stopped her car in front of O'Malley's dented car. The inspector opened up the hood and connected the starting cable with the battery of the other car.

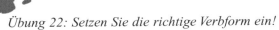

Übung 22: Setzen Sie die richtige Verbform ein!

A few minutes later, O'Malley's car was ready to start again.

"I think I was in luck, that the two of you just happened to be driving by," he said finally. "Wouldn't have liked walk home in this fog. Where are you headed, anyway?"

Now that his car (1. run) _____ again, the man became quite talkative, thought Hudson.

"Yeah, we want to go to Castle Bludstone. It can't be very far from here, can it?"

O'Malley (2. take) _____ a step back from the inspector. "You want to go to Castle Bludstone? At this hour? Do you want to stay there overnight?" he asked.

Elvira (3. look) _____ at the man astonished and shrugged her shoulders.

"Sure. The castle is a luxury hotel now, right?"

O'Malley laughed. "Oh yes, and what a hotel indeed. Listen, over there in the village there (4. be) _____ a charming little guesthouse. It's no luxury hotel, but a reputable house. Wouldn't you rather stay there overnight?"

"Why should we?" asked the inspector. What was wrong with the man all of a sudden?

O'Malley looked at James and Elvira questioningly.

"You really don't know, do you?"

"What don't we know?" Elvira asked back. "Listen, mister, I (5. get cold) _____ and I need a warm bath. Your car is working again and I would like to get on the road."

O'Malley simply shrugged his shoulders.

"Great, but don't say I didn't warn you."

Then he (6. get into) _____ his car and started the motor. Before he drove away, he (7. roll) _____ down his window one last time.

"Good luck, Mister Hudson and Miss Elliot. And take the advice of a friend: (8. beware) _____ of Gabriel Ratchet …"

"Beware of whom?" Elvira asked, puzzled.
Shivering and perplexed, Hudson and Elvira were left standing on the lonely street.
"Gabriel Ratchet?" Elvira asked once more. "Who the hell is this guy?"
Inspector Hudson felt a chill run over his back. And this time, it wasn't because of the cold fog.
"Oh, Elvira, I fear that Gabriel Ratchet is no 'guy' at all … he isn't even a human …"
Elvira looked at the inspector, confused.
Elvira steered the car carefully over the hills.
"Well, James," she asked impatiently. "Who or what is this 'Gabriel Ratchet'?"

James cleared his throat. He tried to add a dramatic tone to his voice, but the inspector was simply too shy and factual.

Übung 23: Drücken Sie Ihr Problem mit den richtigen Worten aus!

1. Sie haben sich verlaufen.
   a) ☐ I'm not sure about this receipt. Is this the right one?
   b) ☐ Excuse me, I seem to be lost. Could you give me some directions?
   c) ☐ What do you think about these trousers? Do they match?

2. Sie verstehen nicht, was gesagt wurde.
   a) ☐ Would you hand me that bag?
   b) ☐ Is this the best way to the square?
   c) ☐ Could you repeat that, please?

3. Eine Rechnung im Hotel scheint falsch zu sein. Was sagen Sie?
   a) ☐ I think you've made a mistake. This isn't my size at all.
   b) ☐ Could you bring us another bottle of wine?
   c) ☐ Could you please recheck this?

4. Sie sind nicht sicher, ob Sie den Inhalt eines Briefes verstanden haben.
   a) ☐ Could you please explain this letter for me?
   b) ☐ Could you reread this letter to me?
   c) ☐ Could you write me a letter?

5. Die Dame in der Bank hat Ihnen zu wenig Geld rausgegeben.
   a) ☐ Excuse me, but I think you made a mistake.
   b) ☐ Pardon me, how much longer is the bank open?
   c) ☐ Excuse me, could you check my account balance?

"Gabriel Ratchet is, first of all, a popular northern English folk tale. It has to do with a ghostly dog, that – invisible to human eyes – lives above the clouds. Only during wild storms you can hear his terrible growl."

"Brrr, how extraordinary," said Elvira.

"Yes, and it gets even better. It is said, whoever hears the growling of Gabriel Ratchet, is destined for death and must die soon."

"Stop it, James! You are scaring me. What a gruesome story. And it actually looks as if a storm were about to come through. Look at the sky."

Inspector Hudson glanced through the front window upwards the sky.

In the last quarter hour, they had been driving almoust continuously up into the mountains and had left the fog behind them in the valley.

Only single whisps of fog lingered on the road like strayed souls. But then, bleak clouds began to cover the rising full moon.

Übung 24: Gespräche über das Wetter: Beantworten Sie die Fragen mit den Wörtern in Klammern!

1. How is the weather in England? (foggy with low temperatures)

   _____

2. What kind of weather is London known for? (rainy)

   _____

3. What type of weather is perfect for a picnic? (sunny, a few white clouds)

   _____

4. What kind of weather do you hope for at Christmas? (snow)

5. What kind of weather is dangerous at the beach? (stormy)

Hudson laughed.

"That fits together quite excellently. One could say our host had ordered the weather himself."

Elvira Elliot threw an astonished sideways glance at the inspector.

"Ordered the weather too? What do you mean by that, James?"

Hudson couldn't hold back his smile. The man on the street, O'Malley or whatever his real name was, had played his role very well. But he had made a small mistake.

"Now, Elvira, that small event on the road belongs to the staging of the murder mystery. I suspect that our 'Mr O'Malley' will receive all the other visitors with the same act – and tells all of them this ghost story. Although I must admit, that the good man is a quite talented actor."

"An actor? You mean, he only pretended that his car broke down? But how can you tell, James?"

"Oh, he betrayed it to me with a small detail. I introduced myself with my family name and also my first name. But as we took leave of Mr O'Malley, he also mentioned your last name. How could he know it – if he doesn't belong to the castle hotel's acting troupe and has our name from the guest list?"

Elvira slapped her forehead.

"Of course. He called me by my last name. That didn't occur to me at all. Oh boy, the planners really put a lot of effort into this."

"Indeed," asserted Hudson. "Even the story with Gabriel Ratchet is pretty true to form."

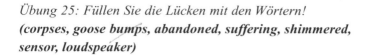

Übung 25: Füllen Sie die Lücken mit den Wörtern!
(corpses, goose bumps, abandoned, suffering, shimmered, sensor, loudspeaker)

The inspector smirked to himself. They would probably hear an ugly dog bark coming out of hidden speakers in the course of the next two days.

In the end, the 1. _____ were just part of this little adventure. Elvira was distracted again anyway.

"There it is!" she called and pointed in front of her.

Indeed. At the tip of a small hill lay the old Castle Bludstone. Strictly speaking it was not quite a castle, but a huge estate, built out of stone, framed on the left and the right side by two compact towers.

Nevertheless, the old ruins breathed the spirit of centuries past.

A light rain had begun and the grey facade of the estate 2. _____

_____ palely in the moonlight.

"Not bad," nodded Elvira. "I even read that they have a small swimming pool and a sauna in the basement."

"And probably a couple of 3. _____," joked the inspector.

"Well, as long as they are only actors, it's fine with me," laughed Elvira. "I am looking forward to the first 'murder'.

Do you want to bet that I solve it before you, Inspector Hudson?"

The inspector was just about to answer, when a terrible, drawn-out howling sounded. It sounded like the 4. _____ of a tortured soul.

Or the howling of a giant hound.

Elvira almost 5. _____ the road in fear.

"My God!" she called. "That is the hound from hell!"

Hudson calmingly laid a hand on her shoulder.

"No problem, my dear. I presume, we have driven through a contact beam or a photo 6. _____. The howling is probably coming from a cassette and somewhere on the side of the road is a hidden 7. _____."

"You mean, this all belongs to the show?"

"I am quite sure of it," nodded Hudson. "Our hosts are really putting a lot of effort into this."

"Certainly. At first glance, I would have thought that we were dealing with a real-life hound from hell."

James Hudson smiled. He didn't have to admit that, for a moment, he had been just as afraid as his companion.

Elvira calmed down and steered the car into the drive of the small castle. Already standing there were a brand new Porsche, a middle-market rented car, and a shabby, dented pick-up. Undoubtedly the cars of the other guests.

Hudson observed the cars more closely. Sometimes, one could determine something about the personality of the owner by the kind of car he drove. "It looks like we are the last ones," Elvira said and parked next to the Porsche.

"And that must be our welcome committee," answered Hudson, pointing to an old, upright man in a dinner jacket.

Übung 26: Beschreiben Sie die Autos, die Inspector Hudson beim Schlosseingang sieht!

ÜBUNG 26

a) Pick-up:

b) Porsche:

c) The rented car:

The inspector wanted to ~~step~~ get climb out of the car, but Elvira grabbed him by the arm and held on tightly.

"James, since Miss Paddington surprised you with this short ~~vacation~~ holiday, you probably haven't read the rules for the mystery weekend: in order to make everything as authentic as possible, the mystery is not allowed to be mentioned at all. We are guests in a perfectly normal hotel, OK?"

"That would be just fine with me. Thanks for the warning anyway, Elvira."

Inspector Hudson opened the door. Then – quite the gentleman – he ran around the car to open the door for Elvira.

But the older gentleman had beaten him to it.

"I am very pleased to meet your acquaintance, madam. You must

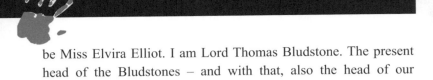

be Miss Elvira Elliot. I am Lord Thomas Bludstone. The present head of the Bludstones – and with that, also the head of our humble, small hotel."

"Very delighted," Elvira said, "but your humble hotel doesn't look ~~that~~ humble at all. It is really beautiful."

Übung 27: Übersetzen Sie die Grußformen!

1. Es freut mich, Sie kennen zu lernen!

   _____

2. Sehr erfreut. Ich habe viel von Ihnen gehört.

   _____

3. Darf ich meine Begleitung vorstellen? Sie heißt Elvira Elliot.

   _____

   _____

4. Guten Tag, Herr Hudson. Schön, Sie endlich einmal zu treffen.

   _____

5. Kennen wir uns schon?

   _____

6. Sie kommen mir so bekannt vor.

   _____

"Oh, thank you," the lord said, pleased. "But you should see it in daylight."
Then he looked towards Inspector Hudson.
"Oh, may I introduce my companion," Elvira said quickly, "this is, Insp — uhhm, James Hudson."

The two men shook hands. The lord's handshake was dry and firm.

"My pleasure to meet you, Lord Bludstone!"

"Indeed it is my pleasure," beamed the lord. "Did you have a good trip? No … eventful happenings?"

"No, no," Hudson said. "Everything went wonderfully. Right, Elvira?"

"Uhhm … yes, certainly, James. Everything as planned."

Elvira and the inspector winked at each other.

"Wonderful!"

Übung 28: Drücken Sie Ihre Wünsche aus!

1. (to enjoy a stay)

   I trust that you _____

2. (to have a trip)

   I hope that you _____

3. (to have sleep well)

   I wish that you _____

4. (mother) (to do) (good)

   I trust that your _____

5. (to go) (to the castle)

   I had hoped _____

"Come, you must be quite exhausted from the long journey. It's pretty far from London to here. I will show you your room and you can freshen up a bit. I would suggest that you …"

The lord went silent as a bone-shaking howling sounded through the twilight.

Pale as death, the old nobleman almost dropped Elvira's luggage and looked around, shocked.

Elvira giggled and leaned over to James.

"Not this dog hunt again," she whispered. "And the old lord isn't playing his role that badly at all."

But Inspector Hudson wrinkled his brow. Maybe Lord Bludstone really was a talented actor, but his reaction to the sudden howling seemed quite real to the inspector.

Half an hour later, James Hudson knocked on the door to Elvira's room.

Elvira opened the door. Her hair smelled of a nice shampoo and she had slipped into a simple but elegant evening suit.

"You look magnificent, Elvira," James Hudson said and meant every word of it.

Übung 29: Machen Sie Elvira Komplimente!

1. (to smell great) *You smell great!*

2. (to have lovely hair) _____

3. (to wear a handsome suit) _____

_____

4. (to have on an attractive outfit) _____

_____

5. (to make a funny joke) _____

ÜBUNG 29

To his surprise, she blushed a bit.

The inspector cleared his throat and opened the door for the insurance agent.

"Ahh, are you ready, my dear? Lord Bludstone wanted to show us through the house a bit before dinner. Ah, there he is now."

Indeed, in this moment the lord was coming up the stairs.

"As I see you are both ready. Then we can start right away. I'll make it short, you're probably quite hungry."

Shortly thereafter, Elvira and James followed the lord through the castle, astonished. Whoever the architect was, he understood how to equip the castle with the most modern luxuries without destroying the charm of the old estate.

Besides another half dozen guest rooms, there were two salons, a game room, and a small library with an impressive collection of classics and modern literature.

Lord Bludstone was especially proud of the former ~~arches~~ vaults of the cellar, in which the small swimming pool and the sauna were to be found.

Übung 30: Schreiben Sie die Sätze ohne verkürzte Verben!

! ÜBUNG 30

1. We can't make it because we're late.

_____

2. Let's go to the castle and we'll just have a relaxing weekend.

_____

3. We've got to check in before dinner.

_____

4. You needn't go to all the trouble. We're fine with what we have.

_____

5. I can't go with you because I've already got plans.

6. Don't go to that store, they'll overcharge you every time.

"This cold autumn weather," said Lord Bludstone, "creeps into one's bones. There is nothing better than a good round of sweating to get rid of the chills. You should try it sometime if you get the chance."

"Oh yes," laughed Elvira and looked at the inspector, "we will take your advice to heart, right James?"

James Hudson blushed, even without the heat of the sauna.

Übung 31: Unterstreichen Sie die Adjektive!

To distract from himself, he pointed to a thick iron door, that led further to the sauna area. The door was obviously very old and didn't fit with the modern-equipped rest of the cellar.

"And, uhhm, where does this door go, Lord Bludstone?"

The lord waved them aside.

"Oh, behind there is the castle's old ice cellar. It was used as storage for perishable food items, but today, we have a modern freezer in the kitchen. Apropos kitchen: we should probably end our tour and head towards the dining room. I am sure that Miss Johnes, our lovely housekeeper and cook, has prepared a lush welcome banquet. You will get to know the other interesting guests over dinner."

"Gladly," Elvira said.

Then the three climbed the last steps to the ground floor.

Übung 32: Finden Sie die Synonyme und setzen Sie die richtige Ziffer ein!

1. scent
2. fake
3. deceive
4. foliage
5. protrude
6. climb
7. be sure

	trick
	stick out
	plants
	smell
	be positive
	go up
	artificial

As they went past one of the doors that led to one of the small towers, the inspector noticed an aromatic, somehow exotic scent, one that he had smelled before.

"Excuse me, Lord Bludstone," he asked, "but what is that interesting scent?"

"Why yes, I smell it now too," she said.

A smile spread across the lord's face.

"Nice of you to notice," he beamed. "Most people today aren't capable at all of perceiving such fine smells."

Then he looked at his wristwatch.

"We are in danger of angering Miss Johnes ... but if you can hold back your appetite for another few minutes, I would like to show you something. In the western tower are my private rooms – and my secret passion. Come!"

Hudson and Elvira looked at each other questioningly, while Lord Bludstone pulled an old key out of his pocket and opened the heavy oak door.

Then he led the inspector and the insurance agent into the astonishingly roomy tower part of the building. A spiralling staircase led upwards to the top of the tower.

Übung 33: Wählen Sie das richtige Fragewort aus!

1. _____ way is it to the rooms?

2. _____ are you doing?

3. _____ is for dinner?

4. _____ are you so hungry?

5. _____ is the head of the family?

6. _____ do you get there?

"Am I out of shape," Hudson asked, "or is it getting warmer, the higher we go?"

The lord laughed mysteriously.

"No, Mr Hudson, you are not being deceived. It is getting warmer. You will soon see why."

The trio reached the end of the spiral staircase. Bludstone opened a further door, switched on the light – and Inspector Hudson couldn't believe what he saw.

"My God!" cried Elvira. "That is … beautiful!"

Indeed.

The room at the top of the tower was equipped with giant panorama panels and a glass ceiling. And in the circular room, a true jungle of exotically graceful plants and bushes were blooming. Tropical foliage grew out of tubs or snaked their way to the ceiling on their trellises. The scent that the inspector had faintly smelled was now intense in the apparent artificial air.

"My pride and joy," the old lord said and beamed. "I was a botanist in my youth, you know, and have travelled through the entire world to find and catalogue strange plants. And now that I am too old for such adventures, I have brought the exotic plants to me. Of course it requires a lot of technology to keep my little darlings alive here in this raw climate, but the entire tower is practically just a greenhouse."

Übung 34: Bringen Sie den Dialog in die richtige Reihenfolge!

1. "How wonderful!"
2. "From all over the world."
3. "Yes, your plants are amazing!"
4. "Do you like it?"
5. "Where do they all come from?"
6. "Yes, sure, you're right!"
7. "Oh, let's go to the dining room, we are late."
8. "Look, here they are! My little secret."

Lösung: _ _ _ _ _ _ _ _

"Really, very impressive, Lord Bludstone," said the inspector.
The arrangement and the upkeep of this little botanical garden must cost a fortune.
Apparently, the castle hotel business was going quite well. Or the lord had – like so many nobility – quite a family inheritance available. In any case, he had used his money well.
"Of course, the whole thing is much more beautiful during the day," said the lord, "provided that the sun is shining, which is seldom in this dark area. If you would like, I will show you my little Garden of Eden tomorrow again by daylight. But now we should really head down to the dining room. The other guests are probably waiting with rumbling stomachs."

The dining chambre was lit by a variety of candles, which threw a warm glow into the room.

At the table, which was set with fine silver cutlery and dishes, five guests were already seated and looking curiously as the inspector, Elvira, and Lord Bludstone were led into the room.

"Ladies and Gentlemen, may I introduce: Miss Elvira Elliot and James Hudson, the last two guests of our event-weekend. Miss Elliot, Mr Hudson, may I introduce to you the other guests? First we have Mr and Mrs Wolters. They came especially from Germany."

ÜBUNG 35

Übung 35: Machen Sie aus dem Adjektiv ein Adverb!

1. good   _____

2. deep   _____

3. loud   _____

4. early   _____

5. happy   _____

6. peaceful   _____

7. fine   _____

"Our pleasure," said Mr and Mrs Wolters almost at the same time. The couple smiled friendly in the direction of the new arrivals.

Aha, thought Hudson, the rented car surely belongs to them. In fact, the couple themselves were just as normal as the middle-class rented car that was parked in front of the castle.

The lord continued with his introductions.

Übung 36: Bilden Sie aus den Buchstaben ein passendes Wort!

"I am of course especially proud that Miss Sylvia DeSoto is spending some time with us this weekend. I am not knowledgeable of the scene, but I have (1. drhae) _____ that Miss DeSoto is well on her way, uhhm, so to say, to becoming a pop star."

Sylvia DeSoto grinned widely at the lord. (2. ptcerfe) _____ teeth shone. Sylvia DeSoto was indeed a breathtakingly beautiful young woman with long, brown hair and green eyes that looked almost catlike.

"Oh, you are too kind, Lord Bludstone. But I just brought my new single onto the (3. kertma) _____. Becoming a pop star is still far away, I'm afraid."

Sylvia DeSoto tried to laugh modestly, but she was certainly not very successful at being convincing.

Then she let her eyes fall on James Hudson.

"I am pleased that you are here with us, James," she breathed. "And you too, of course, Miss Elliot."

"As am I," answered the inspector.

The only thing that Elvira Elliot had left for young Miss DeSoto was a cool nod. And DeSoto's (4. dneifryl) _____ smile as well was not very convincing.

43

This Miss DeSoto – Hudson had to admit that he had never heard of her – was without a doubt the owner of the Porsche in front of the door.

Hudson wasn't sure, but he thought he heard a "Puh!" come out of Elvira's mouth.

But Lord Bludstone continued with his introductions.

With a hand motion, he pointed to a round man with thinning hair and a coloured jacket.

"And next is Mr Brannigan from Liverpool."

Mr Brannigan lifted his wine glass and toasted to the new arrivals.

! ÜBUNG 37

Übung 37: Formulieren Sie einen passenden Trinkspruch!

1. (fine weekend)   *To a fine weekend!*

2. (to find the murderer)   _____

3. (to not burst from excitement)   _____

4. (lovely guests)   _____

5. (a wonderful evening)   _____

"Hello everyone," he rambled. "Jimmy Brannigan. It pleases me to meet you, Miss. And you of course, old chum."

"Uhhm, my pleasure," answered Elvira.

"My pleasure as well, Mr Brannigan," said the inspector. "How do you do?"

"I can't complain, man," answered Brannigan and took a deep drink from his wine glass. "To you!"

No doubt, Mr Brannigan was surely the owner of the beat-up pick-up, thought the inspector, smirking.

"And last but not least," said Lord Bludstone, pointing to a young man at the end of the table, "my nephew Michael. He runs the hotel with me. It was his particular idea to organize this kind of weekend. 'Adventure weekend' is what it is called these days."

"Delighted," said Hudson.

The young Lord Michael nodded to him and Elvira in a friendly manner. The family resemblance between him and his uncle was unmistakable.

"Oh, the pleasure is all mine. I hope that you will feel comfortable here with us. Go ahead and sit down. You must be very hungry and thirsty."

Übung 38: Beim Essen: Suchen Sie die passende Antwort aus!

! ÜBUNG 38

1. What can I get for you?
2. May I pour you more wine?
3. Would you like some bread with your meal?
4. Can I take your plates for you?
5. Would anyone like seconds?
6. Would you care for some soup?
7. My compliments to the chef!

☐ Yes, I am finished, thank you.
☐ Yes, please, that would go great with the soup.
☐ I'll have the green salad.
☐ Sure, half a glass would be nice.
☐ Thank you.
☐ I would love some, just a ladle full.
☐ Yes, I'd like more salad, please.

Hudson took his own seat. Sylvia DeSoto, who sat next to him, looked at him conspiratorially.

"I'm so excited for the fascinating murder to happen. What do you think, Mr Hudson ... uhhm, James, which of us is going to catch him?"

The inspector put his finger to his lips.

"Shhhh," he whispered laughingly, "officially, we aren't supposed to know anything about it. At least, someone told me that it is stated in the rules."

Sylvia DeSoto giggled. "True, you are right. I am such a naughty girl."

Out of the corner of his eye, he noticed how Elvira lifted her eyebrow disapprovingly.

Lord Bludstone had taken his place at the head of the table in the meantime.

"Alfred, you may serve us now, please!"

Hudson looked up as an old man in a butler uniform stuck his pointy nose into the dining room for a moment.

"Right away, sir!" said Alfred.

A few seconds later, he began serving the first course, a delicious smelling asparagus crème soup.

And it tasted even better.

!

ÜBUNG 39

Übung 39: Beim Essen: Was sagen Sie in den folgenden Situationen?

1. Dinner is about to begin.
   a) ☐ Have a great trip!
   b) ☐ Enjoy your meals!
   c) ☐ Careful of the mosquitos!

2. The guests are about to drink wine.
   a) ☐ To our lovely hosts!
   b) ☐ To go to the woods!
   c) ☐ To the post!

3. One of the guests is celebrating a birthday.
   a) ☐ Good Birthday!
   b) ☐ Congratulations!
   c) ☐ Happy Birthday!

4. You are impressed by the soup.
   a) ☐ The soup is divine!
   b) ☐ The soup is hardly edible!
   c) ☐ The soup can be missed!

5. You would like to know how a dish is made.
   a) ☐ Do you have ingredients for this?
   b) ☐ Could I have the recipe for this?
   c) ☐ Do you know what came out of this?

"My compliments to the chef," said Hudson. "This soup is really tasty."

The butler, who had politely held himself in the background, took a step forward.

"Pheasant in a light thyme sauce, my lord. I took the liberty of trying a bit of it already and have to say, Miss Johnes has outdone herself again."

"My dear," giggled Sylvia DeSoto, "that sounds delicious. If I don't watch out, in two days I will gain all kinds of weight here!"

Elvira smiled at the little pop-star.

"But my dear, you don't need to worry at all about your figure."

"You're just saying that, Elvira. You don't need to stand on stage three times a week. The spotlights are shameless – you see every gramme."

"Nonsense!" Mr Brannigan, the business man, slurped his soup and grinned at Sylvia DeSoto. "I am sure that you look fantastic onstage, my dear."

Übung 40: Welches Wort ist das „schwarze Schaf"?

1. tell, say, drink, report, shout   _____

2. sad, happy, blue, well, bad   _____

3. great, fine, wonderful, ugly, powerful   _____

4. love, peace, pain, hate, apple   _____

5. introduce, complain, walk, promise   _____

6. friend, brother, sister, mum, grandma   _____

7. rude, ill-mannered, polite, blunt   _____

"Please excuse me for a moment," said Lord Bludstone and put down his napkin. "I have to go borrow some candles."
The lord pulled one of the six candles carefully out of the candelabra and wrapped the underside of it in a napkin.
"See," he smirked, "the perfect little torch. I'll be right back."

again!

48

Übung 41: Korrigieren Sie die Fehler im Text und unterstreichen Sie die fehlerhaften Stellen!

Then he lefts the dining room.
Because of the missing Kandle, the entire room had become a bit more mysterious.
"Well, an candlelight dinner is really quite enjoyable, right?" Brannigan was asked loudly and elbowed Sylvia DeSoto.
Alfred the buttler had just been served the delicious looking pheasant when a terrible howl kame through the dinink room.

Sylvia DeSoto screamed shrilly.
Elvira Elliot rolled her eyes.
Eva Wolters grabbed her husband's hand instinctively.
"Man, there's someone else who is hungry," joked Mr Brannigan, without removing his eyes from the pheasant. Michael Bludstone, the young lord, looked up with mild surprise. Alfred, the butler, raised one eyebrow slightly annoyed. He appeared not to like it at all, that the act had to start during dinner. Inspector James Hudson registered all of these reactions in the matter of a second. The inspector had of course attempted to remove himself from the "Murder-Game" as much as possible, but he was not able to fully suppress his detective instincts.
Whoever was let in on the game hadn't betrayed himself through his reaction.
"W-What was that?" asked Eva Wolters, who pressed closely to her husband.
Alfred, the butler, cleared his throat.
"According to the legend, that was the howling of Gabriel Ratchet, the hound from hell. The superstitious people from these parts believe that the howling of the hound precedes a soon, violent death."

Eva Wolters scooted closer to her husband.

Inspector Hudson suppressed a smile and threw a side glance at Elvira Elliot. The insurance agent could hardly hide her smile as well. The butler had given this explanation rather even-temperedly, apparently he didn't think much of this kind of staged entertainment.

The inspector understood him well. He simply hoped that the act, which had apparently just begun, would leave him time to try the delicious pheasant.

Mr Brannigan looked like he thought the same.

"Well, then let's start, before this dog shows up here in the flesh and eats the bird. I'll serve myself, if that's all right."

The business man grabbed the knife to cut himself a bit from the pheasant.

At the same time, Eva Wolters wanted to grab for her wine glass. The arms of the German lady and the business man hit each other so hard that Eva jerked back and knocked over the candelabra.

With a murmur, the rest of the five candles went out.

It was dark as night.

Sylvia DeSoto let out a short squeak.

"Oh no, how clumsy of me!" cried Eva Wolters in the darkness.

A few of the chairs were shoved to the side, Brannigan swore.

!

ÜBUNG 42

Übung 42: Ersetzen Sie die Wörter in Klammern durch Synonyme!

Inspector Hudson felt a hand grab onto his and pressed hard under the table. It was Sylvia DeSoto's hand. At almost the same moment, Elvira (1. grabbed) _____ his other hand in the dark. "Just stay near me," whispered Elvira.

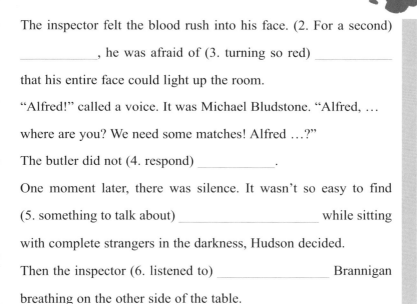

The inspector felt the blood rush into his face. (2. For a second)
_____, he was afraid of (3. turning so red) _____
that his entire face could light up the room.

"Alfred!" called a voice. It was Michael Bludstone. "Alfred, …
where are you? We need some matches! Alfred …?"

The butler did not (4. respond) _____.

One moment later, there was silence. It wasn't so easy to find
(5. something to talk about) _____ while sitting
with complete strangers in the darkness, Hudson decided.

Then the inspector (6. listened to) _____ Brannigan
breathing on the other side of the table.

"Man, these are the torments of Tantalus," groaned the business
man. "I can smell the delicious bird, but I can't cut a single piece
off of it."
Steps were heard from another room. Then a match was struck. In
the light of the small flame, the butler's face was recognizable.

Übung 43: Beim Essen:
Übersetzen Sie die Ausdrücke ins Englische!

1. Bitte reichen Sie mir ein Stück Brot.

_____

2. Gibt es noch Fasan?

_____

3. Probieren Sie einmal die Suppe. Sie schmeckt herrlich!

_____

4. Nein danke, ich bin satt.

_____

5. Möchten Sie etwas trinken?

_____

"Excuse me, sir," he said in Michael Bludstone's direction. "I was in the kitchen and borrowed a match from Miss Johnes."

"You're a real treasure, Alfred," said Michael, while the butler grabbed onto the candle and lit them all again.

James Hudson ascertained to his relief that Elvira and Sylvia DeSoto had let go of his hands at the same time. Luckily, neither of them had noticed the attempts of the other to get closer to him. Then he looked around himself. Brannigan's eyes were fixed on the pheasant in the light of the candle.

Eva and Bernd Wolters looked at each other and smiled.

Strange, Hudson thought, didn't the two of them sit the opposite way around before the lights went out?

Well, maybe he was deceiving himself. The two Germans were really so inconspicuous that it was hard to watch them – even if one wanted to.

Michael Bludstone looked at the door to the hallway, through which Lord Bludstone had just disappeared. "Strange," he said finally, "where is my uncle? If you would excuse me for a moment, please, I'll go and see. Maybe he is having trouble with the safe."

Then he took one of the candles out of the stand and left the room. "I ask you all not to let the pheasant get cold," said Alfred the butler. "His lordship will surely be right back."

At this moment, came another blood-curdling scream. And this time, it was human.

Again, Hudson looked up to observe the reactions of the people present.

The guests reacted more relaxed this time.

Übung 44: Bilden Sie verkürzte Sätze!

1. Being our guests, you need not serve yourselves.
   Being our guests, you needn't serve yourselves.
2. Elvira had not eaten since the picnic earlier that day.

   _____

3. We will just have to start without you.

   _____

4. Where is my uncle? I thought he had stepped out for a moment.

   _____

5. It is important to eat with good table manners.

   _____

Sylvia DeSoto giggled in a silly way, Eva Wolters laughed at her husband, insecurely, and Mr Brannigan paused just a second before he let the carving knife slide into the pheasant once again.

The first howl of the "hound from hell" had a real shock effect, but the second scream left the guests rather cold.

Only Alfred looked surprised. Obviously disturbed, he stepped towards Elvira Elliot.

"M-May I serve you a bit of pheasant, madam?" he asked, stuttering.

"Gladly," Elvira answered and looked at the inspector in amazement.

She looked ~~like~~ *as if* she was thinking the same as Hudson. Suddenly, Alfred was playing his role perfectly. Slowly, it seemed like he was starting to enjoy the little act.

The butler had just cut a thin slice of the pheasant for Elvira as Michael Bludstone stumbled into the room. His hair was wet and unruly. Apparently, it had started to rain heavily outside.

Michael's suit was completely wet.

"My God," he called. "Come quickly. My uncle is … he is …"

Inspector Hudson jumped up. Either the actors of this murder mystery had become complete acting geniuses or something had *really* actually happened!

! *Übung 45: Was ist britisches Englisch, was amerikanisches?*

ÜBUNG 45

1. litre   _____
2. fall   _____
3. crisps   _____
4. truck   _____
5. loo   _____
6. soccer   _____
7. tap   _____
8. freeway   _____
9. petrol   _____

"What happened?" asked Hudson.

Michael swept a wet lock of hair from his brow.

"Lord Bludstone … my uncle … he is lying outside in the rain and isn't moving."

As if on command, lightening struck at this moment, right in front of the window. A drawn-out thunder rolled over the hills. A gust blew around the walls of the castle.

With a bit of fantasy, the howling of the wind sounded like the moaning howl of a violent dog.

Inspector Hudson kneeled down next to the lifeless body of Lord Bludstone.

Hudson took the hand of the lord and felt his pulse.

"You could have come up with a more pleasant setting for your crime game," called Brannigan. Apparently, he would rather devote himself to the dinner in the warm dining room.

James Hudson swallowed.

The hand of the old lord had become ice cold. The inspector's index finger continued to search for a pulse, without success.

Übung 46: Ordnen Sie den Dialog!

1. "Calm down, Michael, first we have to check for a pulse."

2. "I'm sorry, your uncle is dead."

3. "Do you feel anything?"

4. "Uncle, can you hear me? We have to do something!"

5. "No! Uncle!"

6. "Come on, let's bring the body inside."

Lösung: _ _ _ _ _ _

"I am afraid," Hudson called to the house, "this is no game anymore. The man is really dead!"

"No! Uncle!" called Michael Bludstone.

"Oh, my God!" panted Elvira. "What are we going to do now?"

Übung 47: Setzen Sie die richtigen Präpositionen in die Lücken!

The wind had become so strong that the words were ripped ~~themselves~~ out 1. _____ the insurance agent's mouth. Hudson had trouble understanding her.

"First of all, we should bring the corpse 2. _____ the house before we all catch our death 3. _____ cold. And looking for clues here is impossible now."

Hudson looked 4. _____, wrinkling his brow. The crackling rain had left the clay ground around the scene of the crime completely soft. Deep puddles had formed and had hidden all tracks 5. _____ the castle forever that might once have been there.

Together with Michael Bludstone, James Hudson carried the lord's lifeless body 6. _____ the building.

A crackling bolt of lightning lit up the unreal corpse procession.

The two men laid the dead lord in the hallway. Sylvia DeSoto and Eva Wolters looked away.

"Oh," Brannigan said, unmoved. "Are you sure that this isn't

just a part of this wonderful and well organized crime-game?"
"How dare you say that?" called Michael Bludstone. "My uncle is dead! This isn't a game any more!"
"Calm down, Michael." The inspector laid his hand on the shoulder of the new head of the Bludstone family. "The death of your uncle is really an unusual coincidence. Even I thought at first that it was just a show."
Brannigan lowered his eyes.
"I'm sorry," he said to Michael. "I didn't mean it like that. I just wanted to be sure."
James Hudson thought for a moment.
Now they had to deal with an actual case of death, so the game could end as well.
"I'd like to ask for all of your attention for a moment," he called.
The others present looked at him, surprised.

Übung 48: Welche Buchstaben sind nicht hörbar?

1. listen   _____
2. half   _____
3. castle   _____
4. iron   _____
5. might   _____
6. should   _____
7. psycho   _____
8. lightening   _____

Then the inspector took his badge out of his wet jacket pocket and showed it. "I am an inspector at Scotland Yard – and this badge is real, in case anyone should have a doubt. Until we find the cause of the … sudden death of Lord Bludstone, I would like to ask all of you to make yourselves available for my inquiries. Please do not leave the castle – but of course with this weather, that's not really an option."

Michael, Sylvia DeSoto and Mr Brannigan looked with astonishment at the inspector's identification. The Wolters seemed particularly interested in it.

Übung 49: Setzen Sie die richtige Verbform ein!

At this moment, Alfred, the butler, came into the hallway. If the sudden death of his lord (1. affect) _____ him, then he didn't show it. In one hand he (2. hold) _____ another candle holder, in the other a few dry towels that he handed to Elvira, Michael and the inspector. Then he spread a large bed sheet over the corpse of Lord Bludstone.

"Alfred, could you try to fix the fuse again?" he then asked.

The butler nodded.

Then he took a candlestick out of the holder and disappeared through the kitchen door.

"What are we (3. do) _____ now?" asked Elvira Elliot.

"First of all, we need to inform the local police," said James Hudson.

At this moment, the electric chandelier (4. hang) _____

from the ceiling in the entrance hall lit up. Alfred, the butler, had

apparently fixed the fuse. The inspector breathed deeply. In this

way, a little light was shed on the subject.

Michael Bludstone (5. do not) _____ pause for a moment and

went to a telephone on the other end of the entrance hall.

"I'll call the police right away," he called.

But he had barely picked up the receiver when his face went blank.

He pressed on the cord a few times.

That wasn't a good sign, (6. think) _____ the inspector.

"Damn!" yelled Michael Bludstone. "The line is dead!"

"It's dead too?" Mr Brannigan asked, not very sensitively.

"I'm afraid, gentlemen, that is no strange occurrence for the storm

that's (7. blow) _____ around out there."

Alfred, the butler, stepped into the entrance hall again. In his hand
he held the broken fuse.
"The castle is still connected to the digital network with a power
line. And lightning loves to strike the old posts."
"No problem!"
Elvira reached into her bag, that she almost always had with her,
and took out her small, shiny, silver mobile phone.
Hudson noticed how the butler shook his head sympathetically.
Elvira glanced at the display of her phone.

"Oh no," she cried. "There's no reception. The castle must be stuck in an area without it."

"I'm afraid that's the case, my lady," nodded the butler.

"Th … that means we're really cut off from the outside world?" said Sylvia DeSoto.

Übung 50: Übersetzen Sie die Redensarten in die andere Sprachrichtung!

1. not give a damn about something

2. to be keen on something

3. Immer mit der Ruhe!

4. to take a quick one

5. All is well that ends well.

6. Ich drück' dir die Daumen.

"It looks like it," answered the inspector and looked around. "At least the storm is letting up a bit."

The other guests looked at him expectantly. He had identified himself as an authority from Scotland Yard, and now the others were obviously waiting for him to take the lead.

In any case, he could give up ~~the~~ (any) hope ~~for~~ (of) a restful weekend. James thought for a moment what he should do.

"Alfred, could you help me bring the remains of Lord Bludstone into the cellar? There his body will be preserved for forensics."

"F-For forensics?" stuttered Eva Wolters. "Do you believe that the lord was … murdered?"

The inspector looked at the young German sternly.

"At least I can't rule out … an unnatural death at this point. And you have to admit that the conditions of his death are very unusual."

Bernd Wolters pulled a box of matches out of his jacket pocket and lit a cigarette.

Übung 51: Wie kommen Sie zu Scotland Yard?
Beschreiben Sie den Weg!

! ÜBUNG 51

1. Geradeaus, links in die Fußgängerzone und an der Ampel rechts.

   _____

   _____

2. Biegen Sie rechts in die Haverford Street. Es ist am Ende der Sackgasse.

   _____

   _____

3. Gehen Sie über die Brücke und es ist auf der linken Seite.

   _____

   _____

4. Fahren Sie mit der U-Bahn bis zur dritten Haltestelle und nehmen Sie die Treppe in Richtung Buckingham Palace.

_____

_____

5. Gehen Sie zurück bis zur Kreuzung und dann links.

_____

_____

The inspector looked up, surprised.

"But that means," Wolters said, blowing out a cloud of smoke, "that the murderer is still among us."

Inspector Hudson breathed deeply.

"I can't rule that out as a possibility either," he said finally.

Hudson got a chill as he and Alfred left the cellar again. The inspector and the butler had placed the lord's remains on an old table and had covered them with a table cloth.

"What an undignified crypt," Alfred said and took a last look at his dead master.

"Lord Bludstone really deserves much better."

"It's just temporary," consoled the inspector. "As soon as the storm has settled, we will go into the village and inform the police and the coroner. As soon as everything is settled, Lord Bludstone will receive an appropriate final resting place. I assume that there is some kind of family crypt here, Alfred?"

The butler nodded his head.

"Of course, sir. There is even a small mausoleum directly behind the castle. All those of the Bludstone line are entombed there."

"Apropos relatives: Did the lord have any?" Hudson asked with a furrowed brow.

Übung 52: Welche Aussagen passen?

1. Bei der Polizei
   a) ☐ I would like to report a missing child.
   b) ☐ We are interested in buying some stocks.
   c) ☐ We need to inform you about a death at our castle.

2. Auf der Post
   a) ☐ I would like to send this package to Germany.
   b) ☐ I am interested in your finest bottle of red wine.
   c) ☐ Could you give me that box marked fragile?

3. In der U-Bahn
   a) ☐ Mind the gap.
   b) ☐ Fasten your seat belt!
   c) ☐ All aboard!

4. Am Bahnhof
   a) ☐ The train departs in an hour and a half.
   b) ☐ The next tour is in forty-five minutes.
   c) ☐ The exchange rate has changed since yesterday.

5. In der Werkstatt
   a) ☐ Your wrist has been broken.
   b) ☐ Your battery needs to be recharged.
   c) ☐ There are insects attacking your trees.

"Just his nephew Michael, I'm afraid," answered Alfred. "He is the last of the noble line of the Bludstones."

"And the only heir, I assume?"

"Of course, sir. Michael Bludstone was – "

The butler stopped mid-sentence and looked at the inspector, outraged.

"Sir! You don't really believe that Michael had something to do with the death of his uncle –? What a monstrous thought!"

James Hudson looked at the butler sternly. It wouldn't be the first time that greed was greater than the bonds of family. As an inspector, he had dealt with enough similar cases of the sort.

"I don't believe anything, Alfred," he said quietly, "but I have to look at every possibly motive within the framework of the information that I have."

Alfred cleared his throat. "Of course, sir. I understand. You are just doing your duty. But I have to tell you something."

The butler paused.

Hudson looked at him in anticipation.

"What then, old chap?"

"Well, honestly it is a bit embarrassing to talk about it. I seem so indiscrete, you know?"

Hudson pulled the butler back into the cellar and closed the door.

!

ÜBUNG 53

Übung 53: Verneinen Sie die folgenden Fragen mit einer entsprechenden Antwort!

1. Do you believe that Sir Michael may have killed his uncle?

   _____

   _____

2. Had you thought about any other heirs to the throne?

   _____

   _____

3. Do you think that the evidence will incriminate Michael?

_____

_____

4. Do you think that the inspector has found any clues?

_____

_____

5. Do you think that Alfred is keeping a secret?

_____

_____

"Out with it, Alfred. No one will hear it apart from us – and I am naturally sworn to silence … if you should possibly have something to say that would incriminate Michael Bludstone. Then I would certainly have to commit your statement to my report."

Übung 54: Bilden Sie Verkürzungen aus den Verben in Klammern!

ÜBUNG 54

Alfred shook his head.

"Incriminate? No, I (1. not believe) _____ so at all. More like vindicate."

The butler cleared his throat one more time and took an innocent glance at his former employer, whose silhouette was still outlined by the table cloth.

"Sure, Sir (2. Michael is) _____ theoretically the only heir of the Bludstone's fortune – but in reality he may not get much of it."

The inspector wrinkled his brow. "What do you mean by that, Alfred?"

"Well, the Bludstones were once a very rich family, but in the course of several hundred years, its fortune suffered. In other words: The Bludstones are almost bankrupt. (3. That is) _____ why Sir Michael had the idea to change the castle into a hotel a few years ago. And when the success (4. did not) _____ come, it was his idea to stage these distasteful … mystery games, to attract more guests."

"I understand. You're right, Alfred. That really does remove Michael from the list of suspects. I suspect that he will be happy when he doesn't inherit his uncle's debts."

"That's exactly the way it is, sir," Alfred nodded sadly. "It's really a shame. But the changing of the castle into a hotel and the construction of the greenhouse in the tower rooms rapidly decreased the Bludstone's last financial means. And I fear that Michael has invested the rest of the family fortune in a couple of bad stocks."

The inspector nodded sympathetically. The quick rise and fall of the stock boom had led many inexperienced stockholders into ruin. Hudson was happy that Elvira always ignored stock tips and hadn't touched them a bit.

The two men left the cellar. The butler took an old key out of his pocket and shut the door.

Hudson was happy to leave the cellar behind him.

The temperature in the old arches was really unpleasantly low. No wonder that cellars of that sort were used for the storage of food.

*Übung 55: Formulieren Sie ein Versprechen! Nutzen Sie die Satz-anfänge **I promise that**, **You have my word that**, **You can trust that**!*

1. (to keep his secret)

   _____

2. (not to tell the others)

   _____

3. (to be silent about Michael's finances)

   _____

4. (to consider all motives and suspects)

   _____

5. (to search the entire house for clues)

   _____

6. (to not stop until the culprit is found)

   _____

7. (to take investigations very seriously)

   _____

"You have helped me quite a lot," said the inspector thankfully. "Always of service," answered the butler. "I would just like to ask you not to inform the other guests about the Bludstone's financial situation. That wouldn't be very good advertising for the hotel." "Of course, Alfred. Don't worry. I will be silent as the grave." The two men started up the stairs, which led into the main hallway.

"Oh, one more question," the inspector continued, "what was the actual murder mystery? I mean, who was supposed to be murdered according to the screenplay – and who was the murderer?"

The butler cleared his throat. It was obviously an unpleasant theme for him. As a butler of the old school, this kind of disclosure was obviously more than embarassing.

"Well, the whole thing seems kind of macabre in light of the present circumstance. The horrible mystery's plot follows a kind of Sherlock Holmes classic, that is probably very familiar to you, isn't it?"

"Correct, sir. According to the plot, Michael Bludstone wanted to force his uncle, the lord, to have a heart attack by sending a fake "hound from hell" at him, so that he would be the only heir, to drive a nail into the family fortune, as they say."

"I understand," responded Hudson. "That is certainly macabre. It looks like reality imitates fiction. Good that there is no such thing as this hound from hell, right?"

ÜBUNG 56

! *Übung 56: Korrigieren Sie die Sätze und schreiben Sie in korrektem Englisch!*

1. Lord Bludstone have left the dining room.

   _____

2. The inspector started right away to his investigations.

   _____

3. In case for the lord's death, his heir would inherit his debt also.

   _____

4. There is none such thing like the hound from hell.

   _____

5. We will definitely think after the lord's dying.

"Well, sir," Alfred said hesitantly. "I wouldn't go so far as to say that Gabriel Ratchet, the hound from hell, does not exist. I saw him with my own eyes!"

The inspector swallowed and looked at the butler with large eyes. "You can't be serious, Alfred?" he said astonished.

The butler looked at the ground.

"I'm afraid so, sir. It was a couple of weeks ago. I was raking the autumn leaves in the park behind the castle, near the family vault. The sun was already going down and the evening fog had come in. Suddenly, I heard a deep growling behind me and turned around. A shadow slipped past the Bludstone's small mausoleum and piercing eyes, glowing like coal, stared at me for a second. I froze and will never forget this moment. Then the creature growled one more time and disappeared into the fog."

"Unbelievable," said the inspector. "Are you sure that you didn't just see a stray dog? In the fog, eyes can play tricks on them."

The butler shook his head.

"Oh, I am sure that it was a dog, sir, but it surely did not come from this world. You should know, sir, that the Bludstone's family history has always been connected to that of Gabriel Ratchet. It is said that with the appearance of the dog, an old secret will be brought to light, one that the founding father once took with him to the grave."

Hudson lifted an eyebrow and rubbed his chin. What a mysterious story. But there was time for that later.

Inspector Hudson and the butler stepped into the entrance hall of the castle. The rest of the guests and Michael Bludstone stood around without purpose. The fright because of the sudden death could still be seen in their faces.

"There you are again, finally, James," Elvira said, relieved. She pointed to a window next to the main entrance. "The storm has only got worse. There is no way to leave the castle in these conditions."

Hudson looked outside. The wind from the storm whipped thick rain drops against the glass, in regular intervals, the angry lightening struck across the black sky.

Basically, the inspector was quite happy about the bad weather, since none of the suspects could slip out in it.

James Hudson made a decision.

"Ladies and Gentlemen," he said in a loud voice to speak over the booming thunder. "The ... surprising death of Lord Bludstone obviously occurred at the same moment as the blackout. Each of you had the opportunity, to take advantage of this moment and creep past Lord Bludstone and murder him. I fear, therefore, that each of you comes into question as a suspect. At least for now."

The guests reacted with surprise and outrage.

!

ÜBUNG 57

Übung 57: Unterstreichen Sie das passende Wort!
Vorsicht – die Wörter klingen gleich!

1. Hudson went to the beach/beech.

2. Elvira drank the hole/whole coffee herself.

3. The sound came from the kitchen. "Did you hear/here it?"

4. Lord Bludstone keeps his wine in the cellar/seller.

5. Nobody nose/knows the murderer.

6. "Do you meet/meat the inspector, Elvira?"

"You cannot be serious," groaned Mr Brannigan and put his hand on his hips.

"I refuse to tolerate such accusations," cried Bernd Wolters. It was the first time that the German showed any kind of emotion.

Übung 58: Formulieren Sie die korrekte Beschwerde!

1. outrage/is/an/This

_____

2. treated/refuse/to/like/a/I/be/criminal/common

_____

3. tolerate/will/such/not/we/As guests,/treatment

_____

4. with/be/handled/deserve/courtesy/We/to

_____

5. mad/must/accuse/such/to/of/things/He/but/us/be

_____

6. going/complain/travel/to/agent/I/am/to/my

_____

7. hear/this/lawyer/My/hear/will/about

_____

He pulled his wife to him and laid his hand on her shoulder.

"My wife and I have nothing to do with this!"

Sylvia DeSoto kneaded her hands nervously.

"Oh, no!" she whispered. "If the public finds out. A story like this is poison for my career!"

"How can you think about your career at a moment like this?" Elvira asked and looked at the pop star angrily. "We're talking about solving a murder here."

The two women exchanged poisonous looks.

Inspector Hudson lifted his hands placatingly.

"Please calm down. Right now this is just a matter of form. I am sure that everything will be brought to light!"

And I will make sure of that, Hudson added in his thoughts.

Then he turned to Elvira Elliot.

"Elvira, would you be so kind as to help me during the interrogation? That would be great."

Elvira beamed.

"Gladly, James. It would be my pleasure."

"Hold on there," yelled Mr Brannigan. "Why isn't she under suspicion?"

The businessman pointed to the insurance agent.

Hudson cleared his throat. He felt his face getting red. "Well," he stuttered, "Miss Elliot couldn't have left the room during the blackout because she … uhhm …"

"… because I was holding the inspector's hand the whole time, that's why!" Elvira finished.

Sylvia DeSoto looked at Elvira with fiery cat eyes. "What, yours too?"

Elvira shrunk back. Then she turned towards the inspector.

"James?! What is that supposed to mean? Is it true what this woman is saying?"

James Hudson rolled his eyes.

"Ladies, I believe that this isn't the right moment. I would like to start the interrogations now."

Elvira Elliot stepped close up to the inspector's shoulder.

"We'll talk about this later, James," she rasped.

The inspector sighed deeply.

"James, I would never have expected that from you – to play around with this little floozy in the dark of the night."

Elvira Elliot's anger wasn't spent yet.

The inspector looked at her imploringly.

Übung 59: Manche Wörter haben mehrere Bedeutungen. Finden Sie sie!

1. to make something different – small money

   _____

2. certain time in prison – a few words

   _____

3. not hot – cough and sore throat

   _____

4. very fast – to show fear or happiness

   _____

5. in the theatre – take part in a sports game

   _____

6. correct – not in the middle

   _____

"Please, Elvira, Miss DeSoto reached for my hand in the dark – at the same moment as you, by the way. What was I supposed to do?"

"Mmpff," grumbled Elvira. "Let's concentrate on the interrogation of the different guests. Do you really believe that one of them had something to do with the horrible death of Lord Bludstone?"

Übung 60: Finden Sie passende Synonyme für das Wort in Klammern!

"We will see, Elvira, we will see," the inspector answered and was glad for the change of topic.

Michael Bludstone had made the library available for the (1. questioning) _____. And the young nobleman was the first, who now opened the door and (2. took his place) _____ next to the inspector at the heavy oak desk. Elvira sat one place further and had a notepad.

James Hudson and Elvira had agreed ahead of time that the insurance agent would just play the role of the report writer – not because a protocol would actually be needed, but so that the interrogation of the guests would (3. assume) _____ a more official character.

And that, James Hudson knew from experience, sometimes worked wonders.

"Please sit down, Michael," Hudson said nicely.

The young lord and last of the Bludstones had indeed no motive to (4. kill) _____ his uncle, but maybe he had other information that could help the inspector along.

"Thank you, inspector," Michael answered and took his seat.

The man surely looked uncomfortable. He rocked backwards and forwards in his chair nervously.

"Michael, your butler Alfred told me about the financial situation of your family. You are the (5. sole) _____ heir of the castle as the last of the family?"

Michael Bludstone looked at the inspector.

"Yes, that is true," he said uneasily. "But the (6. renovation) _____ of the castle hasn't quite been paid for yet. Even after the death of my uncle, the family (7. property) _____ _____ belongs more to the bankers than to me. I have never thought about it before, but I will probably not accept my uncle's inheritance so that I don't have to receive his debts as well."

The inspector nodded.
"Yes, Alfred had told me something similar. But tell me – the idea with the mystery weekends, that was your idea?"
This time the lord's answer came without hesitation. He was obviously still very proud of this idea.

Übung 61: Vorsicht, falsche Freunde!
Unterstreichen Sie die richtige Übersetzung!

1. aktuell – current, actual, up to date
2. also – also, so, then
3. Art – kind, art, type

4. aufstehen – stand up, get up, walk up
5. gültig – guilty, valid, actual
6. Ehepaar – pair, couple, marriage

"Oh yes, Mr … Inspector Hudson. I thought it would be a good idea to attract guests. And Alfred probably told you about the legend that surrounds the Bludstone family. This background is wonderful to market the mystery weekends."

Hudson nodded his head in contemplation. "Certainly. And the real death of your uncle would make the business even stronger."

"I had never thought of it that way," he mumbled.

"That may help you," said Inspector Hudson. "That's it. Would you please send in Mr and Mrs Wolters?"

Michael Bludstone stood up and went to the exit.

"Wait, one more thing," Elvira said after him, "could you make sure that you turn off all those cassettes with the howling dog, Michael? The guests are already frightened enough …"

The young nobleman clapped his hand to his forehead.

"Of course. Good of you to remind me. The castle is dotted with light sensors and contact points that release the howling hound sounds, so the guests are well frightened. I will turn off the devices for them right away."

!

ÜBUNG 62

Übung 62: Beantworten Sie die Fragen mit sinnvollen Antworten! Schreiben Sie die passende Ziffer in das Kästchen!

1. Would you mind handing me those cassettes?
2. Is this the way to the police office?
3. Tell me, were you ever interested in stocks?
4. Is it warm in here or am I out of shape?

5. Who's idea was it to reconstruct the castle?
6. How did you learn about Gabriel Ratchet?
7. Are people fascinated by crime?
8. Does this belong to you?
9. Do you like crime stories?

☐ Oh, the heat is on.
☐ No, I never was.
☐ Sure, right away.
☐ No, it is on the other side of the town.
☐ Yes, they certainly are.
☐ It was mine.
☐ From my grandfather.
☐ No, I like love stories more.
☐ No, it's yours.

Michael Bludstone left the library. Through the half open door, the inspector and Elvira heard him ask the Wolters couple to come into the library.

"Thank you, Elvira," said Hudson. "I hadn't thought of these damn scare tactics again."

"Yes, these recorded howlings are really terrible. When it started during dinner, a cold shiver went up my spine."

The inspector wrinkled his brow. "True, Elvira, they were more than terrible. But one thing is bothering me …"

"And that would be, James?"

"Well, the howling started after the blackout happened."

Elvira Elliot opened her eyes wide.

"You mean that the howling didn't come from a cassette at all? Do you really believe that there is a real-life hound from hell that announced the death of the lord?"

The inspector tilted his head and glanced at Elvira with thoughtful eyes.

"You know how much I love the supernatural, Elvira. I would rather think that something made out of flesh and blood has its hands in the game."

Elvira didn't have any time left to ask the inspector about his suspicions.

With halting steps, Mr and Mrs Wolters, the German couple, came in.

! ÜBUNG 63

Übung 63: Übersetzen Sie Hudsons Befragung!

1. Wie ist Ihr Familienstand?

_____

2. Ich bin ledig.

_____

3. Ich bin verheiratet.

_____

4. Haben Sie Kinder?

_____

5. Welche Staatsangehörigkeit haben Sie?

_____

6. Füllen Sie das Formular aus!

_____

"This night is unpleasant enough for all of us," said the inspector, "I would like to make this as short as possible. How did the two of you get the idea to come to this mystery weekend while you were in Germany?"

"Over the Internet," said Bernd Wolters quickly. "We booked it through a trip planner on the Internet."

"Exactly," nodded Eva Wolters, just as tersely.

"I get it. And may I ask what you both do for a living?"

"We work in the same bank in Hamburg. That's where we got to know each other, didn't we, darling?"

Mr Wolters nodded.

"That's it exactly. At the bank. In Hamburg. It was 1994."

"Mh-mh," nodded Hudson and just observed as Elvira made a few notes. "Did you notice anything strange during the blackout? Or did you notice that one of the other guests left the dining room?"

Übung 64: Äußern Sie Ihre Wünsche!

1. (drink a spot of tea)
   I would like to drink a spot of tea.

2. (take a tour around the house)

   _____

3. (to have slept all day long) (*Vergangenheit*)

   _____

4. (to have known the real Gabriel Ratchet) (*Vergangenheit*)

   _____

5. (to be of service to you all)

   _____

Mr and Mrs Wolters shook their head at exactly the same time.

"I didn't notice anything," said Mrs Wolters.

"I didn't either," Mr Wolters said dutifully.

"Well, thank you for your help up to now. If you would like, you may go back to your rooms now," said the inspector.

"Thank you, inspector," was all that Bernd Wolters said.

Almost in the same second, the couple jumped up and left the room without saying another word.

"Man, were they boring," groaned Elvira angrily after she closed the door behind the Germans. "You have to pull every single word out of them. I really don't want to make any premature conclusions, but these two goody-goodies are much too bourgeois to commit a murder."

"Mmmhh," said the inspector.

Next, Mr Brannigan came into the library.

Unlike the silent Germans, the words poured out of the businessman's mouth.

Übung 65: Finden Sie die passende Verabschiedung heraus!

1. Oh, do you have to leave right away?
   a) ☐ Yes, I am sorry, but I need to stay another week or so.
   b) ☐ Yes, I do, but I can come back again this afternoon.
   c) ☐ No, I have to go immediately.

2. Exuse me, I don't mean to be impolite, but …
   a) ☐ tell me where I can find a phone booth.
   b) ☐ my new shoes haven't nearly been worn in.
   c) ☐ I've got to get going.

3. Why are you in such a hurry?
   a) ☐ I've got some urgent business to attend to.
   b) ☐ I'm asking you a simple question.
   c) ☐ It seemed rather obvious to me.

4. I hope to see you again soon!
   a) ☐ No, not at all.
   b) ☐ Yes, I'm very much looking forward to that.
   c) ☐ Yes, assuming I finish my work.

5. See you later!
   a) ☐ Good-bye!
   b) ☐ You look great!
   c) ☐ To having a good time!

6. Could you do something for me before you leave?
   a) ☐ Granted.
   b) ☐ Surely you must be joking.
   c) ☐ Gladly. What can I do?

Elvira had put down her pen and sighed.
Finally, Inspector Hudson was able to stop the businessman's unending flow of speech and ask a question.

Übung 66: Unterstreichen Sie die Präpositionen!

"Ah, that is all very interesting, Mr Brannigan, I congratulate you on your successes in the, ahm, tube business. But tell me – how did you happen to come to this Mystery Weekend here at Bludstone?" Brannigan settled in his chair and waved his hand.

"Oh, that was my ex-wife's idea, you know? We still get along great and she said one day 'Jimmy, you work too much. Treat yourself to a little vacation.' I think that she heard about this Castle Bludstone in one of her women's magazines. Probably at the hairdresser."

Brannigan laughed. Elvira rolled her eyes.

"And I thought to myself," Brannigan continued, "well hell, Jimmy, it's October and the third business quarter is almost through, and now you have earned enough money for the whole year.

So I treated myself to a couple days of holiday. And who would have thought …"

Brannigan scooted his chair toward the inspector with a squeak.

"… that we would even get a real murder served up to us here. During supper!"

The business man broke out in a hearty laugh. "Bad luck for you, inspector, for you this holiday means that you have to tack on a couple more overtime hours, right?"

Inspector Hudson laughed with effort.

"Well yes, I am going to try to solve the murder as fast as possible so that there is some free weekend left. That will be all, Mr Brannigan. Could you please send Miss DeSoto in?" asked the inspector.

Brannigan got up, breathing heavily, and winked at the inspector conspiratorially.

"I would love, too, old friend. A hot number, that little one, huh? Don't be too hard on Miss DeSoto."

"I will do my best," sighed Hudson.

Brannigan left the library laughing.

"I almost wish that the call of the hellish hound had been for this ugly man," growled Elvira. "This stupid and unpleasant man would definitely be capable of talking the poor lord to death."

"Mmhh," was all the inspector said.

At this moment, Sylvia DeSoto came into the room.

The inspector had a feeling that the temperature in the library had dropped a couple degrees.

The popstar and the insurance agent glared at each other. Then Miss DeSoto turned her attention to Inspector Hudson. Obviously, Sylvia DeSoto had decided just to ignore Elvira Elliot.

Übung 67: Who is who?

1. Hudson is   _____

2. Elvis Presley was   _____

3. Plato was   _____

4. Miss Paddington is   _____

5. Shakespeare was   _____

6. Charlie Chaplin was   _____

7. Elizabeth II is   _____

8. Marilyn Monroe was   _____

The inspector cleared his throat.

"Well, Miss DeSoto, let's make this short. Because of, uhhm, well-known facts I know that you didn't leave the dining room during the blackout …"

"Pah," said Elvira.

"… in spite of that, I would like to ask you if you noticed anything strange at all during the blackout."

Sylvia DeSoto put on an innocent expression.

"What then, inspector?"

"Well, I don't know. Did you notice maybe that someone got up and left the room?"

"To kill the poor lord, you mean? Oh, that is all so terrible. I mean, poor Michael Bludstone already has enough financial problems, right, and now his uncle is dead, too."

"Did you notice anything or not?" Elvira asked impatiently.

"No, my dear," answered Sylvia DeSoto, just as unfriendly. The innocent expression vanished from her face for a second.

"I didn't notice anything. Except for the strong hand of the inspector."

"Ah, thank you, Miss DeSoto. That's all. I suggest that you go back to your room and rest a bit. Maybe you need some …"

"… beauty sleep," whispered Elvira.

"You apparently get up especially early, don't you, my dear?" responded Miss DeSoto evilly.

!

Übung 68: Bitten Sie um etwas mehr Klarheit!

1. (be more specific)
   Could you be more specific, please!

2. (explain that in more detail)

   _____

3. (clear up some questions)

   _____

4. (tell more about the crime committed)

   _____

5. (describe the course of events in detail)

Then the inspector laughed once more.

"Good night, inspector. As long as you are here, I feel absolutely safe."

"How lovely. Good night, Miss DeSoto," nodded the inspector. The popstar left the room and threw one last hate-filled glance at Elvira Elliot.

The insurance agent hurled her pen at the tray on the table.

"Did you see that, James? If looks could kill, then you would have your murderer. Too bad that you were holding her hand during the murder. I would enjoy seeing Miss DeSoto's singing career on the decline. Too bad that it can't be her."

"Mmhh," said the inspector.

Elvira Elliot rolled her eyes. She was angry.

"James, could you please stop with this ominous 'Mmhh'? You are getting on my last nerve. This nerve-racking interrogation was a complete waste!"

"Mmhh …," said the inspector, laughing.

"James!"

"… I wouldn't say that, Elvira. I think this interrogation was incredibly informative."

Elvira Elliot calmed down right away and looked at the inspector, a bit disturbed.

"What do you mean by that? Do you mean to say that one of the guests lied to us?"

"More than that," said Inspector Hudson, "not just one guest. All of the guests lied to us."

Elvira Elliot's eyes widened.

Übung 69: Beantworten Sie die Fragen zum Text!

1. How does the inspector know that Miss DeSoto did not leave the room?

   _____

2. What does Elvira think about the interrogation's success?

   _____

3. What secret does Alfred, the butler, reveal to the inspector?

   _____

4. Whose idea was it to renovate the castle for the Mystery Weekends?

   _____

Inspector Hudson and Elvira went down the broad stairs and into the kitchen. The other guests and Sir Michael had already gone to their chambers. Miss Johnes, the housekeeper and cook, was the only person in the castle that Hudson hadn't questioned yet.

"Come on, tell me, James, what do you mean that all of the guests lied to us? How did you figure that out?"

"Well, let's start with the German couple, who were so terse while answering my questions."

Übung 70: Finden Sie die „falschen Freunde" und die richtige Übersetzung!

1. eventuell   _____   _____

2. bekommen   _____   _____

3. aktuell   _____   _____

4. Gift   _____   _____

5. bald   _____   _____

"Certainly, James. But that fits with those two bores."

"Maybe, Elvira. But this way of answering all of the questions reminds me of the way in which experienced criminals go through an interrogation. They answer all of the questions as briefly as possible, as not to get themselves caught up in dangerous contradictions. And they always try to clear their answers with each other right away."

Elvira stopped on one of the stairs.

"You mean … the Wolters are criminals?"

The inspector shrugged his shoulders.

"Maybe you are right, and Mr and Mrs Wolters are just extremely boring people. But something else makes me wonder. Do you remember how Mr Wolters lit 1. _____ a cigarette during the questioning?"

"Yes, and?"

Elvira shrugged her shoulders.

"Well, during the delicious dinner, the electricity went out and we sat 2. _____ in the dark, and it took a couple of minutes until

Alfred, the butler, came back with matches from the kitchen …"

"My God, you are right, James. When Bernd Wolters had matches in his pocket the whole time, why didn't he pull them 3. _____ _____ in the dark dining room to make some light?"

The inspector nodded.

"Exactly. Obviously he didn't think 4. _____ that. Anyway, I thought that the Wolters switched places 5. _____ Alfred came back with the matches."

"You mean that the Wolters used the darkness to creep 6. _____ and kill the lord?"

Inspector Hudson lifted up an eyebrow and tilted his head.

"I wouldn't go that far, Elvira. Since Miss DeSoto and Mr Brannigan lied to us during the questioning as well."

"In what way, James?"

"Well, we know that Miss DeSoto couldn't have left the dining room before the blackout …"

Elvira just let out a "Phhh!"

"… but the young lady knows more than she is telling. Do you remember that she felt sorry for Michael Bludstone and the financial misery of his family?"

"Ehmm, yes, she mentioned something like that," nodded Elvira.

"But the Bludstones made every effort possible not to tell their guests about their financial woes. How could she know about that?"

"That nasty snake. And what's with Mr Brannigan?"

"He also leaked something out in his neverending speech, my dear.

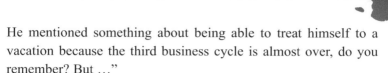

He mentioned something about being able to treat himself to a vacation because the third business cycle is almost over, do you remember? But …"

"… but we are already in October," called Elvira. "We have been in the fourth quarter for weeks. A businessman like Mr Brannigan shouldn't make such mistakes!"

"Exactly," nodded the inspector. "The question remains, why these people all lied to us – and what is really going on."

"I'm getting the impression that none of the guests are here because they want to be."

Deep in thought, Inspector Hudson and Elvira Elliot reached the kitchen.

The inspector opened the door. Miss Johnes, the housekeeper, was putting dirty dishes into the dishwasher.

"What a shame," she mumbled as she scratched some food remains from a plate. "The beautiful pheasant. Hardly touched. And I was cooking that dinner for hours."

Miss Johnes found it unnecessary to greet the inspector and Elvira.

*Übung 72: Vergleichen Sie die Personen mit **whereas**!*

1. Miss Paddington (round and pleasant) and Miss Johnes (tall, thin, and strict)

   _____

   _____

2. Elvira (doesn't flirt openly) and Miss DeSoto (flirts openly with Hudson)

   _____

   _____

3. Inspector Hudson (shy, calm) and Mr Brannigan (loud and nervous)

_____

_____

4. The greenhouse (magnificent at night), (more magnificent by day)

_____

_____

5. The guests (scared when they heard the first howl), (not scared for the second howl)

_____

_____

"Oh, yes, Miss Johnes, quite a shame," said the inspector. "But these, uhmm, tragic circumstances ruined all of our appetites. I am Inspector Hudson from Scotland Yard, by the way, and this young lady is Miss Elvira Elliot."

"Yeah, yeah, Alfred told me everything already," said Miss Johnes. "That is the curse of the hound from hell. Michael and the lord shouldn't have upset the old Gabriel Ratchet with these silly mystery games. I always warned them – but no one listens to me!" the housekeeper nagged.

"Terrible, Miss Johnes, really terrible," said Inspector Hudson. "But tell me, did you happen to notice anything strange?"

The housekeeper took a step towards the inspector and Elvira. The light over the sink threw a strange shadow over her face.

"If I noticed anything strange? Did I ever. For weeks this damn hound from hell has been hissing and howling in the fog – and I don't mean these stupid special effects from the cassettes that Michael Bludstone has installed all over the place. No, I mean Gabriel Ratchet, the true hound from hell that hungers for human souls. I tried to warn Lord Bludstone. Again and again. But he was only interested in the plants in his greenhouse up in the tower. I don't even want to know how much that glass box did cost him." Inspector Hudson sighed softly. There was no use in asking Miss Johnes any more. Besides that, the old lady seemed so peculiar to him. One look at Elvira showed him that the insurance agent thought the same thing. *yeah*

Übung 73: Ordnen Sie richtig zu!

! ÜBUNG 73

a) tourist b) kitchen c) beach d) university e) to fire someone
f) guest house g) to move in h) tenant i) employee j) return ticket
k) profession l) timetable m) railway n) vegetable patch o) television

1. In den Ferien   _____

2. Zu Hause   _____

3. Im Job   _____

Hudson quickly took his leave.
"Thank you, Miss Johnes," he said. "You helped us a lot. Good luck, Ma'am." *Madam*
"Beware of the hound from hell," Miss Johnes called after him as he left the kitchen with Elvira. "Beware of Gabriel Ratchet!"
The inspector closed the kitchen door behind him. He didn't see that Alfred, the butler, stepped out of a small room in the kitchen and smiled at Miss Johnes conspiratorially.

Elvira Elliot tried to shake away her goose bumps. "What a strange person," she mumbled.

"Certainly," the inspector agreed. "Now I know how much I should appreciate my dear Miss Paddington."

The two of them had reached the entrance hallway. The inspector pointed to the old door that led to the cellar.

"Will you come with me into the cellar, Elvira? I would like to look at the poor lord's corpse one more time. I didn't see any kind of signs of outside violence, but I just want to be completely sure. Maybe I overlooked a trace of something."

"Bbrr, James. You really know how to treat a lady. I hope that the visit to a corpse isn't your idea of a romantic evening."

The inspector cleared his throat bashfully.

"In no way, Elvira."

!

ÜBUNG 74

Übung 74: Wie lauten die Sätze richtig?

1. As/stood/cellar/in/the/occurred/idea/him/to/an/he

   _____

2. temperature/The/increased

   _____

3. everything/in/was/order/wanted/sure/that/I/to be/that

   _____

4. seemed/until/he/all/It/normal/looking/went/clues/for

   _____

5. shocked/What/discovered/him/he

   _____

James Hudson opened the wooden door and snapped on the light. He noticed in the first moment that something was wrong. Elvira noticed too that a warm breeze of air wafted towards them.

"My God, is it warm," she called. "Well, at least I'll get rid of my goose bumps."

But Hudson didn't answer her and stormed down the steps. The unusual heat could only have one cause.

With quick steps, the inspector crossed the small swimming hall and went towards the wooden sauna room.

It was true!

Someone had changed the regulator for the temperature to as hot as possible and had left the door wide open. The open sauna emitted a tropical heat that had already gone through the entire cellar.

And even worse: the same person had opened the door to the ice cellar next door.

The inspector wiped a drop of sweat from his brow and closed the door to the sauna. Then he turned the temperature down to zero.

"What a waste of energy," Elvira said breathily. "Who would do such a thing?"

"A good question, Elvira," answered the inspector. "Apparently, someone tried to raise the temperature in the ice cellar."

Übung 75: Unterstreichen Sie die Sätze im Text, in denen etwas aktiv getan wird!

!

ÜBUNG 75

"But why?"

"That's another good question, Elvira, for which I don't have an answer right now."

The inspector stepped into the ice cellar. The temperature in the old archways had risen dramatically since the first time he had been down here. The centuries of coldness were able to spite the sudden storm of sauna heat and had kept everything relatively dry. The temperature of the ice cellar was still noticeably lower than that of the heat in the swimming pool.

The inspector shook his head.

"Obviously, someone tried to heat the lord up a bit, if I can be that blunt," Hudson said.

James Hudson shook his head. He was clueless. But something that Miss Johnes had said was bothering him. According to the statement that Miss Johnes made, Lord Bludstone had only been working in his greenhouse for the past couple of weeks – although the hotel was in danger of going bankrupt and financial ruin threatened him. Maybe the lord only wanted to distract himself with his hobby, but maybe there was something else behind all of it. Whatever it was, the inspector decided that there was still time for that tomorrow.

Hudson closed the door to the cellar behind him.

"Come, Elvira, it's time to go to bed. All these riddles will not run away from us. And with this storm, the suspects won't be able to run away from us either."

Inspector James Hudson was dog-tired, but it wasn't time to think about sleep. He had brought Elvira Elliot to her room and had departed from her with a goodnight kiss on the cheek.

With a nice feeling in his stomach, he went into his room and slipped into his pyjamas.

Then the inspector lay on the soft pillow with open eyes and ruminated. The case just didn't leave him any peace.

Sighing, the inspector stood up and put on a guest bathrobe with the Bludstone family coat of arms that he had found in the bathroom before.

Übung 76: Finden Sie das Synonym!

1. arrogance
2. pain
3. faith
4. excellence
5. pleasure

☐ ache
☐ pride
☐ quality
☐ trust
☐ joy

Then he slid into his slippers and slowly opened the door to the hallway.

It was silent as death in the castle. The hallway was only lit by the lights on the floor that led to the nearest exit, which were prescribed by law. But the light was enough to find one's way without turning on any more.

On tiptoe, the inspector crept past the doors to the rooms of Miss DeSoto, the Wolters and Mr Brannigan. The private rooms of Michael Bludstone were at the other end of the hall.

The inspector wanted to go up to the dead lord's greenhouse in the tower one more time. It was nothing more than his detective instinct, but the inspector suspected that there was a further clue waiting for him up there.

Suddenly, Hudson heard a door open behind him. Although he had no reason to hide, he slipped behind the suit of armour. It would probably be quite interesting to see who was taking a night tour.

Light fell out of the open doorway, and in the next moment, Mr Brannigan, the supposed business man, slipped out of his room. Hudson's took a moment to adjust to the sudden light and to recognize what Mr Brannigan had in his hand. It was a camera.

Brannigan looked all around cautiously. He was wearing the same loud suit, making him visible even in the dark. He probably didn't own any other one.

Übung 77: Beschreiben Sie, was die Personen gerade machen!

1. (Right now) (to walk through the hall) (Mr Brannigan)

   _____

   _____

2. (At the moment) (Inspector Hudson) (to watch)
   (the happenings in the hall)

   _____

   _____

3. (Presently) (Hudson) (to wait) (in the shadow) (of the armour)

   _____

   _____

4. (Currently) (Elvira) (to sleep) (in her room)

   _____

   _____

5. (At the present) (Michael) (not to be found)

   _____

6. (Right now) (Lord Bludstone) (to lay) (in the ice cellar)

   _____

7. (Miss De Soto) (at the moment) (to dream of being a star) (and)
   (to sleep)

   _____

Hudson ducked deeper into the shadow of the armour. Brannigan looked around one more time and then crept down the hallway.

Übung 78: Setzen Sie die passenden Wörter in die Lücken ein!
(whispered, towards, shook, famous, dampened, cautiously, middle)

In front of Sylvia DeSoto's door, he stopped. The inspector noticed how Brannigan suddenly stood up straight.

Then the supposed businessman changed his professional camera from his right to his left and opened the door 1. _____.

Apparently he wasn't just leaning on it, which the inspector hadn't noticed at first.

"This is the chance!" Brannigan 2. _____ into the night and took a step into the room. Hudson had seen enough.

"Have you picked the wrong door, Mr Brannigan?" he asked and stepped out of the shadow of the armour.

"Inspector Hudson!" he called with a 3. _____ voice.

"Ahh, yes, it looks as though I have. It was so dark that I did get the wrong door."

"Well, my good man," said the inspector and stepped 4. _____ Brannigan, "it looked to me as if you knew exactly which door you had turned into. That is Miss DeSoto's room, if I am correct. Would you be so kind as to explain to me what you are doing with Miss DeSoto in the 5. _____ of the night?"

"Well …," started Brannigan and hid the camera behind his back instinctively, as if that would help.

"Well, uhhm, I wanted … to ask her, if I could take a photo of her … I mean, maybe she will be 6. _____ someday …" Brannigan fumbled around.

The inspector just 7. _____ his head.

"In the middle of the night? I don't believe that Miss DeSoto would love this idea. OK, so what did you really want?"
Brannigan breathed out deeply.
"Oh, what's the use," he said finally. "I guess I can admit it now. I really did want to shoot a couple photos of Miss DeSoto, but not for my photo album, but for 'Quickflash Magazine'. I am a society reporter, you know."
The inspector was familiar with 'Quickflash Magazine'. A disgusting gossip paper that specialised in dubious stories about the international stars.
"Others would probably call you a paparazzo, Mr Brannigan."
"Fine with me. In any case, I noticed that DeSoto was participating in this mystery weekend. That's why I signed up in the first place – with the hopes of being able to take some hot photos of the little thing. DeSoto is on her way to becoming quite the star, and when she is really famous, you can't get as close to her."
"I understand," nodded the Inspector, "and her photos would be worth a fortune. I don't have to tell you what I think of this kind of 'journalism', Mr Brannigan!"
"Oh, everyone has to know his place, inspector. And besides, with every gossip story and every hot photo, the person's popularity rises. We live from them and they live from us. Besides which …"

"… the bird has flown the coop anyway. I would like to know what little DeSoto is doing in the middle of the night."

The inspector looked into the room.

It was true. The bed was empty and untouched.

Übung 79: Welche ist die richtige Bedeutung der englischen Idiome?

1. "What's the use?"
   a) ☐ It is not worth trying.
   b) ☐ He is asking for the use.
   c) ☐ He wants to know how to use something.

2. "To know one's place"
   a) ☐ Somebody wants to know where he is.
   b) ☐ Somebody asks for a location.
   c) ☐ To be aware of his social status.

3. "I couldn't see my hand in front of my face"
   a) ☐ I am missing a hand.
   b) ☐ My hand was not in front of me.
   c) ☐ It was dark.

ÜBUNG 79

"Well, I would like to know that as well, Brannigan," said the inspector. And he had his suspicions. But he surely wouldn't be telling this 'reporter'.

"I suggest that you go back to your room, Brannigan," Hudson said strictly. "You wish to take some photos of Miss DeSoto, then you can ask her politely tomorrow."

Brannigan shrugged his shoulders in frustration.

Übung 80: Fotografieren: Bilden Sie passende Fragen!

1. Sie möchten einen Film entwickeln lassen.

   _____

2. Sie möchten, dass jemand ein Foto von Ihnen macht.

   _____

3. Sie möchten ein Bild vergrößern lassen.

   _____

4. Sie möchten Kopien von einem speziellen Foto.

   _____

5. Sie möchten eine neue Batterie für Ihre Kamera kaufen.

   _____

"It looks like I have no other option."

Then the reporter went back to his room.

"Good night, inspector."

"Good night, Brannigan."

The reporter stuck his head out of the door once more. "Tell me, my friend – will I get the exclusive rights after you clear up this murder?"

"Good night!" said the inspector once more.

"Okay, okay, it was just a question," mumbled Brannigan, finally closing the door behind him.

Hudson shook his head.

At least now he knew why Brannigan had lied during the questioning.

And he would soon find out the reason for Sylvia DeSoto's lie as well.

The inspector waited a few seconds, and then crept back through the hallway. He had noticed something. A fine stream of light fell through the keyhole of Michael Bludstone's door. Apparently, the young lord was still awake. And the Inspector Hudson had a special suspicion why.

He hated doing what he had to do, but within the framework of a murder investigation, one couldn't always be a gentleman. His sense of duty was more important.

Cautiously, Hudson came close to the door, bent over, and looked through the keyhole.

He had a good view into the young lord's suite. Michael Bludstone sat on his bed and held a glass of champagne in his hand. Next to him sat Sylvia DeSoto in a see-through negligee and toasted with him.

*Übung 81: Was ist richtig? **When** oder **if**? Unterstreichen Sie!*

1. If/When the chef comes, I will complain about the strange butler.
2. If/When Hudson and Elvira leave, she will have to drive the car.
3. If/When the pheasant is made by Miss Johnes, I will try it.
4. If/When Elvira sleeps, Hudson will go to bed too.
5. If/When Elvira has finished her styling, they will start eating.

"To us," he said.

The glasses chimed.

"To us and to my good old uncle, who sacrificed himself for our future. Too bad that he didn't know anything about it and never will."

Sylvia DeSoto broke out in laughter.

"Michael, you are really a terrible guy. I never would have thought it of you when we got to know each other at the premiere party."

She laughed again and kissed the young lord.

Inspector Hudson silently stood up. He had seen and heard enough. Michael Bludstone seemed to be quite pleased about the death of his uncle. But why?

Besides which, the inspector was irritated by the way in which Michael had spoken of his dead uncle.

He crept cautiously through the hallway. For now, he wanted to gather some more information. On tiptoe, he crept down the stairs to visit the greenhouse in the tower.

But he had hardly reached the ante-chamber, when a small sound made him draw back.

Somewhere behind him, a door had squeaked open. The inspector stayed in the darkness and listened to the silence.

Outside, the storm was still howling around the castle.

Well, that was rather easy to determine. Maybe the wind had moved one of the doors.

Warned by the last blackout, the inspector had put a box of matches in the breast pocket of his guest robe as a precaution. He pulled out the box and struck a match. The flame burned quietly and without flickering.

It couldn't have been a draught then, that made the old door open like that.

It seemed as if someone else was underway in the darkness.

The inspector held his breath. Were his ears deceiving him, or did he hear soft steps coming out of the salon?

On tiptoe, he crept into the hallway.

As he reached the salon, he opened the door cautiously a few millimetres, just far enough to risk a look inside.

In one corner of the room glowed two red eyes.

James Hudson jumped back automatically.

"The horrible hound from hell!" was his first thought.

Übung 82: Sie haben sich erschrocken oder sind überrascht worden! Suchen Sie die passende Antwort aus!

1. Sie haben einen Schreck bekommen.
   a) ☐ Oh my Lord!
   b) ☐ Well, fine!
   c) ☐ Yes, that's it!

2. Sie wurden überrascht.
   a) ☐ That's the second time this week!
   b) ☐ I forgot to do it!
   c) ☐ I didn't expect that at all!

3. Sie wurden überrascht und haben vor Schreck Wein auf den Teppich geschüttet.
   a) ☐ I'll get that, just let me stand up a moment.
   b) ☐ I will take care of that. Do you have any rags?
   c) ☐ That's not important, it's two days old.

4. Sie sind unabsichtlich in ein Privatzimmer gekommen.
   a) ☐ Oh, excuse me, I must have lost my way.
   b) ☐ Oh, excuse me, I didn't mean to spill that.
   c) ☐ Oh, I'm sorry, I seem to have forgotten your name.

Inspector James Hudson felt his pulse racing.

"No," he said to himself, "that isn't possible!"

He breathed as softly as possible and then ventured another look through the crack in the door.

The glowing points of light were still there, but this time he recognized exactly what they were. No hellish eyes, just points of light in the darkness.

And they belonged to two pen-flashlights. Soldiers and policemen often use such lights because they give out enough light but are less conspicuous than regular, white flashlights. See but not be seen.

Someone had placed a lot of importance on looking around in the salon without attracting the attention of the other guests.

The inspector needed a few seconds to get used to the darkness in the salon. The two balls of light crossed each other hectically in the room, back and forth, caught on antique vases, stopped shortly on expensive books on the bookshelf and then wandered over very old sculptures and paintings.

The inspector felt like he was the secret witness of a night investigation.

"Look at that," whispered the two shadowy figures with the flashlights in their hands. "These little dog sculptures are worth at least ten to fifteen thousand euro!"

"Euro!" the inspector realized who they were.

Übung 83: Auf der Bank: Suchen Sie die passenden Fragen aus!

1. Sie möchten Geld wechseln.
2. Sie möchten Geld überweisen.
3. Sie möchten Geld vom Konto abheben.
4. Sie möchten Geld einzahlen.
5. Sie möchten Kleingeld haben.
6. Sie möchten Ihren Kontostand wissen.
7. Sie möchten den Kontoauszug haben.

☐ Could I make a bank transfer?
☐ Could I have an account statement?

☐ Could I exchange some money?
☐ Could I have change for this bill?
☐ Could I deposit some money?
☐ Could I withdraw some money?
☐ Could you tell me how much I have in my account?

He had suspected it before, but now he had no doubt as to the identity of the two shadows. Since Great Britain wasn't a member of the European Currency Community – or at least not yet – these two figures could only be Mr and Mrs Wolters.

Übung 84: Ersetzen Sie die Wörter in Klammern durch ein Synonym!

Who would have thought it – the two reserved Germans were obviously professional thieves with a fine eye for antiques. That's why they reacted as they did during his questioning.

And that's (1. the reason that) _____ Bernd Wolters (2. kept) _____ his matches in his pocket during the blackout. They probably used the short amount of darkness to do their first explorations in the castle.

James Hudson thought for a moment what he should do. He was alone, (3. without a weapon) _____, and worse, he was dressed in his pyjamas and a bathrobe. He would (4. surely) _____ make a fool of himself if he tried to arrest them here on the spot. As long as the storm was raging outside, there was no way that they could (5. escape) _____ anyway. If they continued further in their wanderings, he could do it tomorrow.

The inspector lifted his eyebrow. Tomorrow would be quite a hard day of work.

But now, he (6. to plan) _____ to do something else.

Quietly, he moved away from the doorway to the salon and crept to the steps of the tower.

Hudson shied away from turning on the light in the tower entrance so as not to draw the attention of the thieving couple. Then he reached for his matches again and lit his way up the spiral staircase one step at a time.

Finally, he reached the tower room. In the weak light of the match flame, the tropical flowers and bushes came into view.

He looked around. In spite of the storm howling around the castle, the plants stood unmoving.

The inspector lit a new match and bent down to the strange plants that were growing around him. Some seemed like nocturnal plants and were spreading around a honey-sweet, almost intoxicating scent.

Scent.

And that was the word.

Three matches later, the inspector had found what he was looking for. In one of the back corners of the greenhouse, covered by a huge palm tree, bloomed a shrub-like plant. Its bizarre blossoms were organized like grapes and shone blue in the light of the match. Their form reminded him distantly of a medieval helmet.

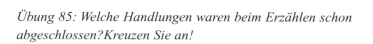

Übung 85: Welche Handlungen waren beim Erzählen schon abgeschlossen?Kreuzen Sie an!

1. ☐ This morning, the sun was shining.
2. ☐ Elvira was shopping downtown.
3. ☐ They were walking through the castle.
4. ☐ Miss Johnes didn't buy any bread.
5. ☐ Hudson spoke to the Wolters.
6. ☐ The Wolters booked the journey in the Internet.
7. ☐ The dog was barking in the middle of the night.
8. ☐ Hudson was really astonished.
9. ☐ He had suspected it before.
10. ☐ Elvira felt her heart beating.
11. ☐ Hudson had a good view into the lord's suite.
12. ☐ It was not the first time that Miss Paddington had tried to do something of the kind.

Next to the pot with these flowers, stood a table, on which was a small, open book.

The inspector ignored the strong scent of the plant and looked into the book. It was a botanical catalogue with the illustrations of many exotic and native plants.

An illustration of the blue flower flaunted itself on the open page. Next to it was a detailed paragraph with the description of the special qualities of the plant.

"Bingo," mumbled the inspector as he began to read the text.

At this moment, the match went out. Hudson wanted to reach into the box and pull out a new one, but the box was empty.

A lightning bolt struck.

For a second, the glass tower was lit up like day.

A shadow fell over the inspector. Hudson turned around.

"You?!" he called, then stars flashed in front of his eyes and everything sank into darkness.

Elvira Elliot stared into the darkness.

Outside, the wind was howling around the old walls and her stomach was growling.

For an entire hour she had been trying to fall asleep, but it was useless. Lord Bludstone's murder and the search for the suspects wouldn't leave her head. Besides which, she hadn't eaten anything since the picnic the day before. And that seemed like an eternity ago.

Sighing, she pushed her bedcovers to the side and got up. The insurance agent, too, slipped into a bathrobe and left the room.

Maybe there was some pheasant left, that they actually should have eaten for dinner. It was worth a try. And Miss Johnes, the housekeeper, had nothing against it when someone tasted a bit of her masterpiece.

!

ÜBUNG 86

Übung 86: Finden Sie die richtige Form und unterstreichen Sie sie!

1. He's so pessimistic/pessimistical about life.
2. May I ask you a theoretic/theoretical question?
3. There is no public/publical transport system.
4. Delicious alcoholic/alcoholical drinks are served.

Quietly, she opened the door and crept out into the hallway.

She believed she heard the clinking of glasses coming from Michael Bludstone's room, but her ears were probably deceiving her. The poor boy really had nothing left to celebrate after the death of his uncle.

Elvira stopped short as lightning struck and the sudden flickering lit up the armour in front of her.

Hopefully the storm wouldn't blow another fuse, otherwise the hallway would be completely dark.

As Elvira Elliot reached the main hallway, she stopped.

Behind the door that led to the kitchen, light was still burning.

Übung 87: Sie möchten jemanden unterbrechen.
Kreuzen Sie die höflichen Formen an!

ÜBUNG 87 **!**

1. ☐ Excuse me, may I interrupt you for a moment?
2. ☐ Hey, shut up a second.
3. ☐ You never stop talking.
4. ☐ If you wait a moment, I have something to add.
5. ☐ Could you please listen to me for a moment.
6. ☐ I see that a bit differently.
7. ☐ You're wrong.

Either Miss Johnes was a very diligent housekeeper, or she suffered from insomnia.

Okay, so she could personally ask Miss Johnes for a little midnight snack instead of creeping through the kitchen like a thief in the night.

Elvira was just about to open the door to the kitchen when she heard a couple of voices behind it. Two, no three people were talking in a lively manner.

Suddenly inspired, she bent down and peered through the keyhole, just like the inspector had just done at Michael Bludstone's door.

What the insurance agent saw surprised her even more.

At the hard wooden table in the kitchen, sat Miss Johnes, Alfred, the butler, and one other man with a coarse face. The man's hair was wet and his face was reddened from the cold wind.

And Elvira knew him.

Übung 88: Unterstreichen Sie Adjektive und Adverbien und sortieren Sie sie!

It was Miles O'Malley, the strange man that had stopped them on her way here because of a supposed defective battery.

So we meet again, thought Elvira curiously, and pressed her ear to the door.

"I caught him as he was up in Lord Bludstone's tower snooping around dangerously. Couldn't have known that the guy is from Scotland Yard."

O'Malley took a deep swallow from his teacup. In front of him on the table was a bottle of whisky, with which he had obviously 'cooled it down'.

Miss Johnes anxiously covered her mouth with her hand. "Miles, how could you? What are we going to do now?"

"Unfortunately, I have to admit," Alfred said in his usual relaxed manner, "the whole thing has slipped out of control. First the death of Lord Bludstone – and now a policeman has been struck down in the tower. It wasn't planned like this at all."

Elvira jumped back.

Oh, no, James, she thought, hopefully nothing serious has happened to you. What a brute!

But now it was important to listen to these three, who were up to no good. Maybe she could use this knowledge to prevent further harm from coming to the inspector and the others.

"And all we wanted to do was the best for the lord and young Michael!" cried Miss Johnes. "And now this. The lord is dead and we are all going to go to jail. If only we had never begun to misuse Gabriel Ratchet for our own purposes. It's the revenge of the hound from hell! He will take revenge on us all for that."

"Please, Miss Johnes, don't be ridiculous," Alfred said calmingly. "That's just an old wives' tale. Though very useful for our purpose."

"Right," O'Malley agreed. "It was Michael Bludstone's crazy idea to change the castle into a hotel and then set up these silly mystery games on top of it. That is a disgrace to the Bludstone family."

Übung 89: Sie befinden sich im Hotel. Finden Sie die passende Antwort und setzen Sie die Ziffern ein!

ÜBUNG 89 !

1. Do you have any rooms for tonight?
2. How many nights will you be staying?
3. Is breakfast included?
4. Where is the lift/elevator?
5. Will you be paying with credit card?
6. What sort of room would you like?
7. Can you put another bed in the room?
8. What time's breakfast?
9. By what time must I be out of the room?

☐ Just the weekend.
☐ No, it is extra.
☐ Just around the corner.
☐ I'm sorry, we have no vacancies.
☐ No, with cash.
☐ From seven until ten in the morning.
☐ I would like a double room, please.
☐ By nine o'clock in the morning.
☐ No problem, sir.

"The more so since one part of the prophecy has now been ful-filled," Alfred added. "The secret, the founding father took with him to his grave, has been revealed. Everything would have turned out great if Lord Bludstone hadn't been killed."

The three emitted a communal sigh.

Elvira had no idea what Alfred, Miss Johnes, and O'Malley were up to, but the inspector would be interested in it.

Quietly, Elvira stood up and crept away.

O'Malley had said that he had struck down the poor inspector in the tower room. He was probably still lying there in the dark night and needed her help.

Elvira crept through the entrance hall of the castle, but then sud-denly heard a soft groaning.

The emergency exit sign lit up the great hall only a bit and smoul-dered like little islands of light in the darkness.

The insurance agent listened.

There it was again!

A quiet, barely audible groaning.

*Übung 90: Bilden Sie **if-Sätze**!*

ÜBUNG 90

1. He had been paying attention. He saw the man.

   If he had been paying attention, he would have seen the man.

2. He had been able to defend himself. He wasn't knocked out.

   _____

   _____

3. He took it with him to his grave. We don't know the secret.

_____

_____

4. He was still lying there. He needed her help.

_____

_____

5. She wasn't listening carefully. She didn't hear the sound.

_____

_____

That must be James. Oh, my God, hopefully he wasn't hurt badly. Strangely, the groaning didn't come from the tower, but seemed to come from the door that led to the cellar.

What could that be, thought Elvira. Maybe poor James had wandered through the castle half dazed and had stepped into the cellar by mistake?

Übung 91: Setzen Sie die richtige Verbform in die Lücke ein!

That was very improbable, but who else could be standing on the stair to the cellar, groaning?

Softly, she 1. (to creep) _____ back through the hallway.

"James?" she whispered as she reached the door. "James, … is that you?"

A terrible groaning was the only answer she got.

Elvira swallowed.

Slowly, she (2. to stick) _____ her hand through the cellar door.

A drawn-out thunder (3. to boom) _____ over the hills.

Elvira pressed down the door handle and slowly pulled the door open.

"James?" she whispered again.

The shadow of a stumbling figure became marked unclear on the cellar stair.

Then lightening (4. to strike) _____ again. Its light gleamed through the window for a fraction of a second and (5. to light up) _____ the hall like daylight.

Elvira Elliot wanted to scream, but her voice failed her.

The only thing (6. to come out) _____ of her throat was a squeak as she (7. to recognize) _____ the figure that stood up in front of her. Lord Bludstone.

Elvira looked into the face of the groaning lord for a fraction of a second, then she (8. to lose) _____ all her senses. Darkness covered her.

Inspector Hudson had the strangest visions. Elvira and Sylvia DeSoto were pulling on his hands like in a tug-of-war. A hound from hell in a butler's uniform and with Alfred's face was playing the judge. Mr Brannigan was shooting pictures and laughing. In the background, Lord Bludstone was knocking desperately on the door to the sauna that his nephew was holding closed with all of his might, while the Wolters couple were taking all of the tiles in the swimming pool and throwing them in a sack.

All the while Miss Johnes was hitting a deep gong to announce dinner.

"Enough of that!" moaned the inspector. He knew that this was only a hallucination that had been caused by the blow on his head and the scent of the exotic blossom. Now he just had to convince his unconscious of that.

Slowly, the images began to fade.

Übung 92: Finden Sie die Gegenteile und tragen Sie die passende Ziffer ein!

1. hallucination
2. cause
3. for a second
4. acknowledge
5. strange
6. shiny
7. knocked-out

- [ ] dull
- [ ] eternal
- [ ] ignore
- [ ] conscious
- [ ] reality
- [ ] effect
- [ ] commonplace

The sounding of the gong became what it actually was – just the inspector's throbbing sleep.

Slowly, James Hudson sat up and held his aching head.

This O'Malley didn't just have a coarse face, he also had an arm to go with it. Inspector Hudson had indeed recognized his sudden attacker, but wasn't able to defend himself at the time.

A wave of anger swept through Hudson. Since he came here, the guests had been leading him on the wrong track and lying to him. And now he had been knocked out.

But this was the end.

Hudson lurched groaningly through the greenhouse and finally found what he was looking for. A small, unimpressive peppermint plant in the shadow of a tropical tree. He picked a couple of the prickly leaves and rubbed them against his temples.

The biting pain let up.

Inspector Hudson picked another leaf of the blue flower that he had come here for and put it in the pocket of his bathrobe.

"Piece of evidence number one," he growled.

Then he cautiously went down the stairs.

He had hardly arrived in the entrance hall when he heard a soft moaning.

Elvira!

Übung 93: Beschreiben Sie Ihrem Arzt die Symptome Ihrer Krankheit!

1. (Bauchweh)
   My stomach aches.

2. (Husten, die ganze Zeit)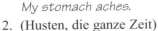

3. (Kopfweh und Schnupfen)

4. (schwindlig, im Stehen)

5. (Beule am Kopf)

_____

6. (starke Zahnschmerzen)

_____

7. (Fieber)

_____

8. (Halsschmerzen)

_____

Hudson lurched through the hall and hurried to Elvira Elliot with quick steps. She had collapsed on the steps to the basement.

Übung 94: Sie möchten sich entschuldigen. Setzen Sie die richtigen Wörter ein!
(by mistake, intentions, accidentally, intented to, my intention, I had meant, accident)

1. I'm sorry I knocked over the candelabra. I did it _____.

2. It was not _____ to disturb you. I simply wanted a midnight snack.

3. If _____ to insult you, you would have known.

4. I _____ lost my way in the castle and overheard voices in the kitchen.

5. I _____ make my way to the library, but got lost.

6. My overhearing the chatter in the kitchen was an _____

_____.

7. The road to failure was paved with good _____.

"Elvira!" he cried. "What happened?"

"James! Thank God you are all right. That's a nice lump you have on your forehead," she joked.

Then it apparently struck her again what she had seen.

"Lord Bludstone!" she called. "I saw him. In the flash! I mean, his ghost, or … whatever …"

Inspector Hudson laughed at Elvira soothingly and helped her stand up. He didn't seem to be surprised at all.

"Okay, Elvira, just stand up first. You will catch your death of cold on the cold tiles."

Then the shaking insurance agent led Hudson to a small sitting area in a corner of the hall.

Übung 95: Finden Sie passende Synonyme für die Wörter in Klammern!

"D-Did you not hear what I said, James?" she asked, (1. dumbfounded) _____. "I saw the dead Lord Bludstone. He was standing right in front of me like you right now!"

"Well, sure, Elvira, I believe you that you saw Lord Bludstone – but I don't believe that he was dead. At least not really."

"W-What (2. are you implying) _____, James?"

Elvira looked at the inspector with wide eyes.

"Well, I think that the good lord has been hit with something, but is otherwise very much alive. He can't be (3. that) _____ far from here."

James Hudson looked through the darkened hall and finally discovered the shadow of a figure that was curled up on (4. the steps) _____.

"Ah, there he is now," said Hudson, as if it were the most normal thing in the world.

"Th-That's impossible," she gasped.

Hudson excused himself quickly and went to the figure on the stairway. It was (5. indeed) _____ Lord Bludstone. His face was pale, his lips were blue, and his entire body shook. In spite of that he was as fresh as a daisy.

"I-I a-am so cold," stuttered the lord.

Hudson sat down next to him and laid his hand on his shoulder, as if to cheer him up.

"I surely believe that, Lord Bludstone. And you were really cold-blooded when you agreed to go into such a dangerous game. And on top of that, you chose the wrong players. I (6. suggest) _____ that I bring you to your private room, where you can take a nice, hot bath."

"Th-Thank you. Very (7. nice) _____ of you," said Lord Bludstone and let himself be helped up by the Inspector.

While Elvira looked on incredulously, he led the old man to his private rooms.

"Elvira, please do me a favour. Put on some clothes and ask Mr Brannigan to bring the other guests and the (8. employees) _____ _____ together. We will meet in the library in an hour. There are some things to clear up!"

"I believe that as well," she mumbled.

Still (9. incredulous) _____, she watched the inspector disappear with Lord Bludstone into his private rooms.

Inspector Hudson had made a good decision when he decided to let Mr Brannigan bring the guests together. With his preaching way of speaking, he had no (10. scruples) _____ in bringing the other guests and the employees, despite all protests. Besides which, Brannigan was twice as motivated because he – quite justly – had a first-class story for his (11. magazine) _____ _____ under his nose.

Less than an hour later, Michael Bludstone, Sylvia DeSoto, the Wolters, Alfred, the butler, Miss Johnes, and O'Malley were sitting in the bright library.

Übung 96: Drücken Sie Ihre Überzeugung aus!
(to be convinced, to be sure, to know)

1. (the inspector will find the culprit)
   I'm convinced that the inspector will find the culprit.
2. (the mystery surrounding the blue flower will be revealed)

   _____

3. (Lord Bludstone's strange death will be explained)

   _____

4. (things are not as they seem)

   _____

5. (Hudson will get a good night's rest tonight)

   _____

6. (the hound from hell is just a legend)

   _____

7. (Lord Bludstone has chosen the wrong players)

   _____

8. (Elvira saw Lord Bludstone's ghost)

   _____

9. (James likes Elvira very much)

   _____

Elvira and Brannigan stood in the doorway and made sure that no one tried to get away. Outside the castle, the bad weather seemed to be letting up.

"I find this treatment monstrous," protested Bernd Wolters angrily. "My wife and I are paying guests. I am going to complain to my travel agent. It's very annoying!"

"Exactly," agreed Sylvia DeSoto. "What kind of hospitality is that, forcing them out of their bed in the middle of the night?"

Brannigan lifted the corners of his mouth into a grin.

"It wasn't your bed that we forced you out of, Miss DeSoto."

The popstar looked at Michael Bludstone for a moment, then they both looked shamefully at the floor.

"I am sure that Inspector Hudson has a reason for his actions, but what exactly is the reason for this nightly meeting, Miss Elliot?" Alfred asked politely.

Elvira didn't need to answer this question because at this moment, the door opened.

The inspector came in.

"I thank you all for coming, Ladies and Gentlemen," he said. "But we aren't all here yet."

ÜBUNG 97

Übung 97: Drücken Sie Ihre Ungläubigkeit aus! Finden Sie die passende Antwort!

1. Lord Bludstone is still alive.
2. I have discovered your evil plan.
3. You were behind it all along.
4. You began planning for this months ago.
5. Admit it! You are guilty!
6. I have all the evidence I need.
7. Lord Bludstone rose from the dead.

☐ There must be some mistake. I am innocent!
☐ But that's impossible!
☐ I don't understand what you are referring to by 'it'.
☐ That is a ridiculous accusation.

☐ Show it to me and maybe I will believe you.
☐ I will make no such statement.
☐ Can you believe it?

Michael looked around at them, confused.

"What do you mean, inspector? All of the guests and personnel are here."

"Indeed," Hudson nodded, "but you've forgotten the lord of the house. Lord Bludstone."

Inspector Hudson opened the door. Out of the shadow of the hallway, a figure came into the room. Lord Bludstone.

The whole room gasped.

"Uncle!" called Michael Bludstone. "You are alive! But – how … how's that possible?"

"The inspector will clear that up, Michael," the lord said coolly and sat himself down at the head of the table.

"Gladly, sir, but first I would like to clear up some other surprises." The inspector took his seat next to Lord Bludstone.

"I've already spoken with Mr Brannigan about the real reason for his visit. As much as I dislike his motives, his misconducts are slight."

The inspector pointed over his shoulder at Mr Brannigan, who was still standing watching at the wall.

"The reasons for your trip to the castle are a lot more despicable, Mr and Mrs Wolters – if that's your real name at all. I am arresting you here for attempted theft and burglary. I am sure that Scotland Yard will have a thick file on both of you. You'll be able to continue your vacation in jail."

Bernd and Eva Wolters looked at each other, astonished. Instinctively, they jumped up from their chairs.

Mr Brannigan cleared his throat, more like a growl.

Übung 98: Der Fall wird aufgeklärt! Bilden Sie vernünftige Sätze!

1. accuse/attempting/steal/to/I/you/artifacts/castle/the/from/of

_____

2. of/Brannigan's/motives/true/aware/I/already/was/of

_____

3. beginning/Wolters/From/behaved/the/criminals/like

_____

4. calmly/inspector/began/why/Lord/was/Bludstone/still/to/
   explain/the/guests/The/to/was/alive

_____

5. began/evidence/found/castle/unfolding/that/the/He/in/the/he

_____

6. appearance/shocked/sudden/all/guests/the/of/Lord/
   Bludstone's

_____

7. you/here/am/and/I/arresting/theft/for/and/attempted/burglary

_____

8. continue/in/You'll/to/be/jail/vacation/your/able

_____

9. face/were/his/Bludstone's/lips/pale/Lord/blue/and/was

_____

"Forget it," said the inspector. "Mr Brannigan will play Cerberus, so that you won't be let out of here."

"Apropos Cerberus. I don't know if the two of you are familiar with Greek Mythology, but to the Greeks Cerberus was the hound from hell, that stopped the dead from coming back into the world of the living. I supposed you could say he is a relative of your local Gabriel Ratchet."

"What is this nonsense, inspector? Are you giving us a lesson in classical mythology?" Michael Bludstone asked angrily.

"Not at all, Michael. More like botany. But I am sure that I can learn more in this area from you and your uncle."

Hudson reached into his jacket pocket and pulled a strange, blue flower out and placed it on the table.

"I am sure that you know what this is. Aconitum napellus. Because of its form also commonly called 'Blue iron hat'. And you know what the interesting thing is? According to Greek mythology, Hercules once fought with the hound from hell and brought him into the daylight. Out of the hound's angry spit allegedly came this flower. A very fitting murder weapon, when one thinks how the history of your family has been connected with the legend of the hound from hell for centuries, right?"

Michael Bludstone wiped a couple beads of sweat from his brow.

Übung 99: Ein gescheiterter Mordversuch! Bilden Sie Konjunktivsätze in der Vergangenheitsform!

1. Michael was successful. The inspector wasn't on the case.
   Michael would have been successful if the inspector hadn't been on the case.

2. The murder weapon was not clear. The inspector went looking in the tower.

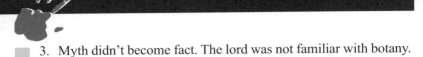

3. Myth didn't become fact. The lord was not familiar with botany.

   _____

4. Elvira never heard the people in the kitchen. She was looking for a midnight snack.

   _____

5. The Wolters behaved suspiciously. The inspector suspected they were criminals.

   _____

"You mean Michael wanted to poison his uncle with the poison from this flower?" Elvira asked.

"Not quite, my dear. The lord really just poisoned himself, right?" Lord Bludstone sighed.

"Yes, that is unfortunately true. At least partly."

Elvira was incredulous. "Partly? What is that supposed to mean?"

"Well, Miss Elliot, in small doses, the poison isn't deadly. It only paralyzes all of the bodily functions and then leads to a deep unconsciousness."

Inspector Hudson nodded.

! ÜBUNG 100

Übung 100: Setzen Sie Synonyme für die Wörter in Klammern ein!

"Heartbeat and pulse become so weak that they aren't discernable

without any kind of (1. assisting) _____ device. And

that was the exact plan. Lord Bludstone wanted to (2. pretend)

_____ his death, so that his nephew Michael would become the sole recipient of his life insurance. The lord would have

been laid down in the family (3. crypt) _____ and the

effects of the poison would have (4. let up) ~~worn off~~ _____ in

a couple of days. And I am sure that Lord Bludstone and Michael

had planned it all exactly so that the amount of insurance would be

sent out of the country, right?”

The lord nodded guiltily.

“That’s exactly the way it was.”

“But unfortunately,” the inspector continued, “Michael Bludstone

met Sylvia DeSoto in the meantime. He would rather have eloped

with her then with his old uncle. That’s why he decided to make a

real murder out of the pretended murder.”

“I knew that that snake was behind this,” Elvira growled.

The inspector ignored the (5. evil) _____ that the two

women exchanged with each other.

“That’s (6. why) _____ Michael crept down into the

cellar again, opened the door to the ice room, and turned up the

sauna. The deathlike conditions caused by the release of the blos-

som’s poison functions only when the body is cooled and the meta-

bolism (7. slows down) _____ .

When it is able to get warm, the organs, which are then running on stored energies, cannot provide the body with oxygen. The victim dies a torturous death."

"That is terrible," gasped Elvira.

The lord looked at his nephew with a mix of anger and sadness. "Luckily, the heating powers of the sauna weren't strong enough. The light warming of the ice cellar only led to the early subsiding of the apparent death, earlier than we had expected, Michael. Lucky for me. And unlucky for you."

Michael Bludstone and Sylvia DeSoto lowered their eyes.

Inspector Hudson stood up.

"Michael Bludstone and Sylvia DeSoto, I arrest you for attempted murder."

"Yes!" cheered Elvira Elliot.

The inspector looked at her reproachfully.

"Excuse me, James," whispered the insurance agent, and turned red.

Then Hudson turned to the lord.

"I'm afraid I have to apprehend you as well, Lord Bludstone. Due For to attempted insurance fraud. I am sorry."

Lord Bludstone nodded.

"You do your duty, inspector. I just wanted to save Michael and myself from ruin. The whole thing was really a dumb idea."

"And on top of that, a completely unnecessary one," mumbled Alfred, the butler, concerned.

The inspector looked at him.

"I would like to have some words with you as well, Alfred."

A couple of hours later, the bad weather had completely let up. After the break of dawn, the telephone lines worked again as well. Michael Bludstone, Sylvia DeSoto, and the Wolters couple found themselves in the custody of the local police. It soon became known, that the real names of the couple were Peter and Regina Brückner; both were indeed being sought by the Interpol for various burglaries. Lord Bludstone as well was questioned by the police, after which he was taken into custody.

Inspector Hudson, Elvira Elliot, and Alfred walked in the morning fog through the park behind the castle. Behind the plumes of fog, the outline of the dark old Bludstone mausoleum could be seen.

Übung 101: Ordnen Sie die Übersetzung zu und setzen Sie die richtige Ziffer ein!

1. This is very important
2. That means a lot to me.
3. This is no small matter.
4. I'm having problems deciding this.
5. The situation is very serious.
6. I must contradict you.
7. I doubt it.
8. I'm quite certain.
9. I feel very discouraged.
10. I agree with you.
11. You are right.
12. I have to think about it.

☐ Das bedeutet mir viel.
☐ Das ist nicht ganz einfach.
☐ Ich bezweifle es.
☐ Ich kann mich dafür nicht entscheiden.
☐ Ich bin mir sicher.

☐ Das ist sehr wichtig.
☐ Ich bin sehr entmutigt.
☐ Die Lage ist sehr ernst.
☐ Ich stimme Ihnen zu.
☐ Ich muss Ihnen widersprechen.
☐ Ich muss darüber nachdenken.
☐ Sie haben Recht.

"And what will happen to Lord Bludstone now?" Alfred asked, concerned.

"Don't worry, Alfred," Hudson answered, "I think that he will get out with probation. He almost paid with his life."

"Yeah, I think so, too," Elvira nodded. "As an insurance agent, I condemn insurance fraud, but I feel so sorry for the lord. His nephew wanted to poison him. Because of this little trollop –"

"Ahem," Inspector Hudson cleared his throat. "Lord Bludstone will certainly have to count on quite a fine."

"Well," Alfred sighed, "that shouldn't be a problem."

He pointed to the mausoleum.

ÜBUNG 102

! *Übung 102: Unangenehme Gefühle. Welche Antwort passt? Kreuzen Sie an!*

1. ☐ Things could be better.
2. ☐ It makes me sad.
3. ☐ Life is treating me well.
4. ☐ I'm concerned about you.

"Gladly, Alfred. I believe you have something more to confess to me, right?"

Alfred nodded shyly.

"I am afraid so. Miss Johnes, Mr O'Malley – he is really the gardener – and I were always against turning the honourable family property into an Mystery Hotel. That's why we always promoted this legend of Gabriel Ratchet, the hound from hell. We thought that after a while, all the guests would be scared away."

Elvira scowled.

"You never believed in the hound from hell? But you would have made the hotel go bankrupt with all of your scary stories. And sooner or later, the bank would have foreclosed on the castle."

"Hardly, my lady," Alfred said.

Hudson and Elvira followed the butler into the stone mausoleum.

The walls were covered with stone slabs, behind which the mortal remains of the Bludstones found their last moments of peace.

Übung 103: Setzen Sie die passenden Vokabeln in die Lücken ein!
(simulate, amusement, disgusted, treasure, skull, mausoleum, weathered)

Alfred pointed to one slab that was particularly old and 1. _____ .

"This is the last resting place of the first Bludstone. Do you remember the legend, that after the hound from hell appears, a secret will be revealed, that the first Bludstone took with him to his grave?" he asked.

"Yes, you mentioned something like that, Alfred."

"Well, shortly after Michael Bludstone had prepared the castle for the silly devices that would 2. _____ the hound from hell, I was cleaning the mausoleum and just happened to bump into this slab. And then …"

The butler pulled on the old slab and pulled it carefully out of the wall.

"… and then something came towards me. At first, I was 3. _____, but then I saw something shimmering in old Bludstone's grave."

The butler grabbed into the old grave. Elvira Elliot feared for a moment that he would pull out an old 4. _____.

Instead, Alfred had a hand full of treasures and gold pieces.

Elvira opened her eyes wide.

Inspector Hudson smiled.

"So that is the secret that the founding father of the Bludstone's took with him to his grave."

"Yes," Alfred nodded. "His grave is full of it. Miss Johnes, Mr O'Malley and I just didn't want to tell the lord. We were afraid that he would let the 5. _____ under Michael's influence, and use it to finally turn the castle into an 6. _____ park."

"No, I don't believe that Michael will have any kind of important influence on his poor uncle now," Hudson said as the three of them left the 7. _____.

Then he looked back into the fog.

"What is it, James, do you want to settle down here?" called Elvira, who had already left with Alfred. "The weekend is over, unfortunately, work is calling. We have to leave again!"

Inspector James Hudson shook his head.

"I'm coming, Elvira!" he called and left the mausoleum behind him. It was probably just his imagination, but he could have sworn that he saw a violent hound in the thick plumes of fog, contently wagging his tail.

THE END

Abschlusstest

Übung 1: Welche Antwort ist die beste?
Kreuzen Sie an!

1. How do you do?
   a) ☐ That's quite simple.
   b) ☐ Fine, thank you.
   c) ☐ Well for now.
2. May I introduce you to my companion?
   a) ☐ What is your name?
   b) ☐ How do you?
   c) ☐ Pleased to meet you.
3. Where do you live?
   a) ☐ Here.
   b) ☐ Far away.
   c) ☐ In London, Kingsroad.

Übung 2: Beschreiben Sie den Weg!

1. Gehen Sie rechts in die Einbahnstraße und auf der linken Seite steht das Gebäude.

2. Steigen Sie bei der Victoria-Station aus und laufen Sie zu Fuß bis Grosvenor Gardens.

Übung 3: Suchen Sie die höflichste Antwort aus!

1. You misheard something.
    a) ☐ What?
    b) ☐ Speak a little louder!
    c) ☐ Pardon me?
2. You would like to interrupt someone.
    a) ☐ If you would wait a moment, I have something to add.
    b) ☐ Can you stop talking at all?
    c) ☐ If you don't stop talking I will walk away.
3. You do not agree with the speaker.
    a) ☐ You are surely wrong.
    b) ☐ I'm afraid I see that quite differently.
    c) ☐ I am fully in accordance with you.

Übung 4: Ich wünschte, ich hätte …! Bilden Sie richtige Sätze!

1. (to spend a quiet weekend at home)

   _____

   _____

2. (to pay closer attention to the guests' behavior during questioning)

   _____

   _____

3. (to be able to tie together all the clues as well as the inspector)

   _____

   _____

4. (to finish dinner before going to bed)

_____

_____

Übung 5: Ordnen Sie den Dialog in einer sinnvollen Reihenfolge!

1. What is your account number?
2. I would like to make a bank transfer.
3. To an account in Germany.
4. Mine is eighty-seven, sixty-four, two-hundred thirty.
5. And where will you be sending the money?
6. Thank you very much!
7. Just write that number down here and it will be transferred directly.

Lösung: _ _ _ _ _ _ _

Übung 6: Sind die Wörter amerikanisch oder britisch?

1. lorry   _____

2. garbage can   _____

3. torch   _____

4. cheerio   _____

5. gas   _____

6. subway   _____

7. undershirt   _____

8. French fries _____

9. elevator _____

10. dustbin _____

11. lift _____

Übung 7: Im Hotel: Welche Aussage ist richtig?

1. When you arrive at the hotel, you say:
   a) ☐ Hello, I have a reservation under the name Fellner.
   b) ☐ Hi, my name is Fellner. How are you.
   c) ☐ Good day, welcome to the hotel.
2. You would like to inquire about phone charges.
   a) ☐ Is there a phone in the room?
   b) ☐ Is the pool open after dark?
   c) ☐ Could you explain the fees for using the phone?
3. You would like to pay with a credit card. What could the hotel clerk answer you?
   a) ☐ I'm sorry, we don't take checks.
   b) ☐ Yes, you may pay for the room all at one.
   c) ☐ Yes, we do take that kind of card.

Übung 8: Ordnen Sie die Sätze den jeweiligen Situationen zu und setzen Sie die passende Ziffer ein!
Post (1) Einkaufen (2) Bahnhof (3) Café (4)

a) I'll have to weigh it. ☐
b) One way or return? ☐
c) We are sold out of … ☐

d) You'd like to order? ☐
e) Are there any letters for me? ☐
f) Keep the change. ☐
g) Anything else? ☐

Übung 9: Setzen Sie wo nötig die richtige Präposition ein!

1. The grocery shop is _____ the corner of Blytonplace.

2. Romeo and Juliet was written _____ Shakespeare.

3. This scientist comes _____ Japan.

4. This tower was built _____ 1745.

5. Look _____ this! It's great, isn't it?

Übung 10: Übersetzen Sie!

1. hin und wieder _____

2. ab und zu _____

3. gesund und munter _____

4. nach und nach _____

5. aus und vorbei _____

Lösungen

Übung 1: 1. a 2. b 3. b 4. a 5. b 6. a

Übung 2: 1. curse 2. simple 3. grab 4. instinct 5. housekeeper 6. shocked

Übung 3: 1. inspector 2. housekeeper 3. radio announcer 4. insurance agent 5. judge

Übung 4: 1. c 2. c

Übung 5: wiped, stepped, held out, accepted, calmed, understand, said, excite, understand, foster

Übung 6: 1. better 2. smarter 3. quicker 4. earlier 5. farther 6. more

Übung 7: 1. hold back 2. are talking about 3. should 4. did 5. stumbled 6. sighed 7. are 8. Do you know

Übung 8: 1. He doesn't like that they are so far from reality. 2. The noises that startled him came from Miss Paddington, who was cooking in the kitchen. 3. His detective instincts make him approach with caution. 4. He names "The Hound of the Baskervilles". 5. No, she names "The Hound of the Basketvilles".

Übung 9: 1. The personal information was taken down by the announcer 2. The mysteries were gobbled up by the young inspector. 3. The answer to the riddle was supplied by the inspector. 4. The breakfast was cooked by the housekeeper. 5. The announcer's question was answered by Miss Paddington. 6. The receiver was picked up by Miss Paddington with anticipation. 7. The door was closed by Hudson quietly.

Übung 10: 1. grumbling 2. inattentive 3. thereafter 4. stood 5. Apparently 6. commit 7. protection

Übung 11: 1. solved 2. cast 3. made 4. interrogated 5. searched 6. caused 7. commenced

Übung 12: 1. quiet, loud 2. seldom, often 3. wrinkled, smooth 4. answer, question 5. noise, silence 6. light, dark 7. weekend, weekday

Übung 13: 1. Miss Paddington won the prize by answering the question correctly. 2. Hudson prefers to leave his work at the office 3. Miss Paddington had already packed his suitcase. 4. It will definitely be a lot of fun! 5. He wanted to carry the suitcase for her but she had done it herself.

Übung 14: 1. Fourteen pounds and fifty-three pence. 2. Two-hundred thirty-six dollars and seventy-eight cents. 3. nine thousand, four hundred twelve 4. four and three quarters 5. the sixteenth of November, 2002

Übung 15: 1. b 2. a 3. b 4. a

Übung 16: 1. a 2. b 3. b

Übung 17: 1. himself 2. her 3. them 4. them 5. he 6. her 7. they 8. it

Übung 18: 1. Let's go a little bit further. 2. Let's have a picnic! 3. Let's wait until the weather is better. 4. Let's drive a little slower, Elvira. 5. Let's have a quick look at the

the map, to see if this way is right.

Übung 19: 1. Elvira, could you please not drive so recklessly? 2. Could you please roll down the window and have a look at the man? 3. Please hand me your baggage and coats. 4. Could you please hand me that bag? 5. Please move to the side of the road.

Übung 20: 1. dress 2. plaid (tartan) 3. tweed 4. jacket 5. leather 6. scarf 7. cap 8. trousers

Übung 21: 1. No, just wait a second, please. 2. Wonderful, thank you. 3. Likewise. It's been so long. 4. Great, the weather was very good. 5. Yes, the directions were fine. 6. Yes, sure, we met last summer.

Übung 22: 1. was running 2. took 3. looked 4. is 5. am getting cold 6. got into 7. rolled 8. beware

Übung 23: 1. b 2. c 3. c 4. a 5. a

Übung 24: 1. The weather is foggy with low temperatures. 2. London is known for its rainy weather. 3. Perfect weather for a picnic is sunny with a few white clouds. 4. I hope for snow at Christmas. 5. Stormy weather is dangerous at the beach.

Übung 25: 1. goose bumps 2. shimmered 3. corpses 4. suffering 5. abandoned 6. sensor 7. loudspeaker

Übung 26: 1. The pick-up is shabby and beaten-up. 2. The Porsche is brand new. 3. The rented car is a middle-class type.

Übung 27: 1. It's my pleasure to meet you! 2. My pleasure, I've heard so much about you. 3. May I introduce my companion? Her name is Elvira Elliot. 4. Good day, Mr Hudson. It's nice to finally meet you. 5. Have we already met? 6. You seem so familiar to me.

Übung 28: 1. I trust that you will enjoy your stay. 2. I hope that you have a good trip. 3. I wish that you would have slept well. 4. I trust that your mother is doing well. 5. I had hoped to go to the castle.

Übung 29: 2. What lovely hair you have! 3. What a handsome suit you are wearing! 4. What an attractive outfit you have on! 5. What a funny joke you made!

Übung 30: 1. We cannot make it because we are late. 2. Let us go to the castle and we will just have a relaxing weekend. 3. We have got to check in before dinner. 4. You need not go to all the trouble. We are fine with what we have. 5. I cannot go with you because I have already got plans. 6. Do not go to that store, they will overcharge you every time.

Übung 31: thick, iron, very old, modern-equipped, old, perishable, modern, lush

Übung 32: 1. smell 2. artifical 3. trick 4. plants 5. stick out 6. go up 7. be positive

Übung 33: 1. Which 2. How 3. What 4. Why 5. Who 6. How

Übung 34: 8. 1. 4. 3. 5. 2. 7. 6.

Übung 35: 1. well 2. deep 3. loudly 4. early 5. happily 6. peacefully 7. fine

Übung 36: 1. heard 2. perfect 3. market 4. friendly

Übung 37: 2. To finding the murderer! 3. To not bursting from excitement! 4. To our lovely guests! 5. To a wonderful evening!

Übung 38: 1. I'll have the green salad. 2. Sure, half a glass would be nice. 3. Yes, please, that would go great with the soup. 4. Yes, I'm finished, thank you. 5. Yes, I'd like more salad, please. 6. I would love some, just a ladle full. 7. Thank you.

Übung 39: 1. b 2. a 3. c 4. a 5. b

Übung 40: 1. drink 2. blue 3. powerful 4. apple 5. walk 6. friend 7. polite

Übung 41: lefts (left), kandle (candle), an (a), was asked (asked), buttler (butler), been served (served), kame (came), dinik room (dining room)

Übung 42: 1. reached for 2. For a moment 3. blushing 4. answer 5. a conversation topic 6. heard

Übung 43: 1. Please hand me a slice of bread. 2. Is there any pheasant left? 3. Try the soup. It's divine/delicious! 4. No, thanks, I am full. 5. Would you like something to drink?

Übung 44: 2. Elvira hadn't eaten since the picnic earlier that day. 3. We'll just have to start without you. 4. Where's my uncle? I thought he'd stepped out for a moment. 5. It's important to eat with good table manners.

Übung 45: 1. britisch 2. amerikanisch 3. britisch 4. amerikanisch 5. britisch 6. britisch 7. britisch 8. amerikanisch 9. britisch

Übung 46: 4. 1. 3. 2. 5. 6.

Übung 47: 1. of 2. into 3. of 4. around 5. in front of 6. into

Übung 48: 1. t 2. l 3. t 4. o 5. gh 6. l 7. p 8. gh

Übung 49: 1. had affected 2. held 3. going to do 4. hung 5. did not 6. thought 7. blowing

Übung 50: 1. sich einen Teufel um etwas scheren 2. etwas sehr mögen, begehren 3. Take it easy! 4. einen schnellen Drink nehmen 5. Ende gut, alles gut. 6. I'll keep my fingers crossed.

Übung 51: 1. Straight, left into the pedestrian zone, and right at the light. 2. Turn right on Haverford Street, it's at the dead end. 3. Go over the bridge and it's on the left side. 4. Take the underground to the third stop and go up the steps in the direction of Buckingham Palace. 5. Go back to the crossroads and then turn to the left.

Übung 52: 1. a/c 2. a/c 3. a 4. a 5. b

Übung 53: 1. No, I don't believe that Sir Michael killed his uncle. 2. No, I hadn't thought about any other heirs to the throne. 3. No, I don't think that the evidence will incriminate him. 4. No, I don't think that he has found any clues. 5. No, I don't think that he is keeping a secret.

Übung 54: 1. don't believe 2. Michael's 3. That's 4. didn't

Übung 55: 1. I promise that I will keep his secret. 2. You have my word that I will not tell the others. 3. You can trust that I will be silent about Michael's finances. 4. You have my word that I will consider all motives and suspects. 5. You can trust that I will search the entire house for clues. 6. I promise that I will not stop until the culprit is found. 7. You have my word that I take my investigations very seriously.

Übung 56: 1. Lord Bludstone has left the dining room. 2. The Inspector started on his investigations right away. 3. In case of the lord's death, his heir would also inherit his debt. 4. There is no such thing as the hound from hell. 5. We will definitely think about the lord's death.

Übung 57: 1. beach 2. whole 3. hear 4. cellar 5. knows 6. meet

Übung 58: 1. This is an outrage! 2. I refuse to be treated like a common criminal! 3. As guests, we will not tolerate such treatment! 4. We deserve to be handled with courtesy. 5. He must be mad to accuse us of such things! 6. I am going to complain to my travel agent. 7. My lawyer will hear about this!

Übung 59: 1. change 2. sentence 3. cold 4. express 5. play 6. right

Übung 60: 1. interrogation 2. sat down 3. take on 4. murder 5. only 6. reconstruction 7. estate

Übung 61: 1. current, up to date 2. so, then 3. kind, type 4. get up 5. valid 6. couple

Übung 62: 1. Sure, right away. 2. No, it is on the other side of the town. 3. No, I never was. 4. Oh, the heat is on. 5. It was mine. 6. From my grandfather. 7. Yes, they certainly are. 8. No, it's yours. 9. No, I like love stories more.

Übung 63: 1. What's your marital status, please? 2. I'm single. 3. I'm married. 4. Do you have any children? 5. What citizenship do you have? 6. Please fill in this form!

Übung 64: 2. I would like to take a tour around the house. 3. I would have liked to have slept all day long. 4. I would have liked to have known the real Gabriel Ratchet. 5. I would like to be of service to you all.

Übung 65: 1. b 2. c 3. a 4. b 5. a 6. c

Übung 66: on, in, to, at, about, in, at, to, for

Übung 67: 1. an inspector 2. a pop star 3. a philosopher 4. a housekeeper 5. an author 6. a comedian 7. the Queen 8. an actress

Übung 68: 2. Could you explain that in more detail? 3. Could you clear up some questions? 4. Could you tell me more about the crime committed? 5. Could you describe the course of events in detail?

Übung 69: 1. He was holding her hand the whole time. 2. She thinks that the interrogation is a complete failure. 3. He reveals information about Michael's finances. 4. It was Michael's idea.

Übung 70: 1. eventually, possible 2. become, get 3. actual, current 4. gift, poison 5. bald, soon

Übung 71: 1. up 2. around 3. out 4. about 5. before 6. out

Übung 72: 1. Whereas Miss Paddington was round and pleasant, Miss Johnes was tall, thin, and strict. 2. Whereas Miss DeSoto flirted openly with Hudson, Elvira did not. 3. Whereas Inspector Hudson was calm and shy, Mr Brannigan was loud and nervous. 4. Whereas the greenhouse was magnificent at night, it was even more magnificent by day. 5. Whereas the guests were scared when they heard the first howl, they weren't scared at all when they heard the second howl.

Übung 73: 1. a, c, f, g, l, m, o 2. b, h, n, o 3. d, e, i, k

Übung 74: 1. As he stood in the cellar, an idea occurred to him. 2. The temperature increased. 3. I wanted to be sure that everything was in order. 4. It all seemed normal until he started looking for clues. 5. What he discovered shocked him.

Übung 75: 1. The inspector stepped into the ice cellar. 2. The inspector shook his head. 3. … Hudson said. 4. James Hudson shook his head. 5. Hudson closed the door to the cellar behind him.

Übung 76: 1. pride 2. ache 3. trust 4. quality 5. joy

Übung 77: 1. Right now, Mr Brannigan is walking through the hall. 2. At the moment, Inspector Hudson is watching the happenings in the hall. 3. Presently, Hudson is waiting in the shadow of the armour. 4. Currently, Elvira is sleeping in her room. 5. At the present, Michael can't be found. 6. Right now, Lord Bludstone lies in the ice cellar. 7. At the moment Miss DeSoto is sleeping and dreaming of being a star.

Übung 78: 1. cautiously 2. whispered 3. startled 4. towards 5. middle 6. famous 7. shook

Übung 79: 1. a 2. c 3. c

Übung 80: 1. Could you please develop this roll of film for me? 2. Could you take a picture/photo of me? 3. Could you enlarge this photo for me? 4. Could you make me a copy of this photo? 5. Could you give me a new battery for my camera?

Übung 81: 1. If/When 2. When 3. If 4. If/When 5. When

Übung 82: 1. a 2. c 3. b 4. a

Übung 83: 1. Could I exchange some money? 2. Could I make a bank transfer? 3. Could I withdraw some money? 4. Could I deposit some money? 5. Could I have change for this bill? 6. Could you tell me how much I have in my account? 7. Could I have an account statement?

Übung 84: 1. why 2. held 3. unarmed 4. certainly 5. get away 6. intended

Übung 85: 4., 5., 6., 7., 9., 12.

Übung 86: 1. pessimistic 2. theoretical 3. public 4. alcoholic

Übung 87: 1., 4., 5., 6.

Übung 88: Adjektive: strange, defective, deep, relaxed
Adverbien: curiously, dangerously, obviously, anxiously, unfortunately

Übung 89: 1. I'm sorry, we have no vacancies. 2. Just the weekend. 3. No, it is extra. 4. Just around the corner. 5. No, with cash. 6. I would like a double room, please. 7. No problem, sir. 8. From seven until ten in the morning. 9. By nine o'clock in the morning.

Übung 90: 2. If he had been able to defend himself, he wouldn't have been knocked out. 3. If he hadn't taken it with him to his grave, we would know his secret. 4. If he had still been lying there, he would have needed her help. 5. If she had been listening carefully, she would have heard the sound.

Übung 91: 1. crept 2. stuck 3. boomed 4. struck 5. lit up 6. to come out 7. recognized 8. lost

Übung 92: 1. reality 2. effect 3. eternal 4. ignore 5. commonplace 6. dull 7. conscious

Übung 93: 2. I cough all the time. 3. I have a headache and a stuffed-up nose. 4. I am dizzy when I stand up. 5. I have a bump on my head. 6. I have got terrible toothache. 7. I have got a temperature. 8. I have got a sore throat.

Übung 94: 1. by mistake 2. my intention 3. I had meant 4. accidentally 5. intended to 6. accident 7. intentions

Übung 95: 1. confused 2. do you mean 3. so 4. the stairway 5. in fact 6. advise 7. kind 8. personnel 9. in disbelief 10. inhibitions 11. journal

Übung 96: 2. I am convinced that the mystery surrounding the blue flower will be revealed. 3. I am convinced that Lord Bludstone's strange death will be explained. 4. I am convinced that things are not as they seem. 5. I am convinced that Hudson will get a good night's rest tonight. 6. I am sure that the hound from hell is just a legend. 7. I am convinced that Lord Bludstone has chosen the wrong players. 8. I am sure that Elvira saw Lord Bludstone's ghost. 9. I know that James likes Elvira very much.

Übung 97: 1. But that's impossible! 2. There must be some mistake. I am innocent! 3. I don't understand what you are referring to by 'it'. 4. That is a ridiculous accusation. 5. I will make no such statement. 6. Show it to me and maybe I will believe you. 7. Can you believe it?

Übung 98: 1. I accuse you of attempting to steal artifacts from the castle. 2. I was already aware of Brannigan's true motives. 3. From the beginning, the Wolters behaved like criminals. 4. The inspector calmly began to explain to the guests why Lord Bludstone was still alive. 5. He began unfolding the evidence that he had found in the castle. 6. Lord Bludstone's sudden appearance shocked all of the guests. 7. I am arresting you here for attempted theft and burglary. 8. You'll be able to continue your vacation in jail. 9. Lord Bludstone's face was pale and his lips were blue.

Übung 99: 2. The murder weapon wouldn't have been clear if the inspector hadn't gone looking in the tower 3. Myth wouldn't have become fact if the lord hadn't been so familiar with botany. 4. If Elvira hadn't been looking for a midnight snack, she never would have heard the people in the kitchen. 5. The inspector wouldn't have suspected that the Wolters were criminals if they hadn't behaved suspiciously.

Übung 100: 1. helping 2. fake 3. tomb 4. lessened 5. nasty 6. the reason that 7. decreases

Übung 101: 1. Das ist sehr wichtig. 2. Das bedeutet mir viel. 3. Das ist nicht ganz einfach. 4. Ich kann mich dafür nicht entscheiden. 5. Die Lage ist sehr ernst. 6. Ich muss Ihnen widersprechen. 7. Ich bezweifle es. 8. Ich bin mir sicher. 9. Ich bin sehr

entmutigt. 10. Ich stimme Ihnen zu. 11. Sie haben Recht. 12. Ich muss darüber nachdenken.
Übung 102: 1. Things could be better. 2. It makes me sad. 4. I'm concerned about you.
Übung 103: 1. weathered 2. simulate 3. disgusted 4. skull 5. treasure 6. amusement 7. mausoleum

Lösungen Abschlusstest

Übung 1: 1. b 2. c 3. c
Übung 2: 1. Go to the right into the one-way street and the building is on the left side. 2. Get off at Victoria Station and walk to Grosvenor Gardens.
Übung 3: 1. c 2. a 3. b
Übung 4: 1. I wish that I had spent a quiet weekend at home. 2. I wish that I had paid closer attention to the guests' behavior during questioning. 3. I wish that I had been able to tie together all the clues as well as the inspector. 4. I wish I had finished dinner before going to bed.
Übung 5: 2., 1., 4., 5., 3., 7., 6.
Übung 6: 1. britisch 2. amerikanisch 3. britisch 4. britisch 5. amerikanisch 6. amerikanisch 7. amerikanisch 8. amerikanisch 9. amerikanisch 10. britisch 11. britisch
Übung 7: 1. a 2. c 3. c
Übung 8: a) 1, b) 3, c) 2, d) 4, e) 1, f) 4, g) 2
Übung 9: 1. at 2. by 3. from 4. in 5. at
Übung 10: 1. now and then 2. now and again 3. safe and sound 4. by and by 5. all over